13

The Brain: A Nonfiction Mystery

CREATIVE NONFICTION™

13

The Brain: A Nonfiction Mystery

CREATIVE NONFICTION™ 13

Editor
Lee Gutkind

Contents

Special appreciation to the
Pittsburgh Center for the Arts *and*
The Lucius N. Littauer Foundation
for support for this special issue.

&

*The Creative Nonfiction Foundation
gratefully acknowledges the*
**Juliet Lea Hillman Simonds Foundation Inc.,
Goucher College's Center for
Graduate and Continuing Studies**
and the **Pennsylvania Council on the Arts**
*for their ongoing support,
as well as the*
National Endowment for the Arts.

From The Editor

The Brain: A Nonfiction Mystery

Lee Gutkind

"*T*hrough a strange legal fluke," Megan Foss, one of the contributors to this issue, recently told me, "Someone sent me my medical records going back some 20 years, and there is a period of time—the best I can figure is about two-and-a-half to three years—that describes events and conditions that not only do I have no memory of, but that I have always had entirely different memories of."

It was a surreal experience for her to sit and read the narrative of her life written by people outside the world of drugs and prostitution—her own personal hellish world since she was a young teenager. Megan endured repeated hospitalizations for endocarditis and surgery on her hands and feet from infected or botched attempts to get a hit on a good vein. Reading about this life that she left so far behind, so long ago—seeing it recorded in black and white—became quite literally shocking and horrifying. But by far, the worst part was her discovery that there were long periods of time—years!—for which she had no memory at all. She began to wonder how much of her past she had obliterated, imagined—and how and why.

"Did I lose memory because of drugs, or did I use drugs to avoid memory?" The irony of this experience is that now, as a writer, so many years after these hidden incidents evidently occurred, Megan says, "I'm driving myself crazy trying to remember," but at the same time, she is afraid to learn what she has so conveniently forgotten. "A nonfiction mystery, if you will."

This concept and phrase—nonfiction mystery—is an apt way of describing this issue and the themes surrounding the brain itself, which, in addition to memory, include behavior, the creative process, intelligence, perspective, etc. No matter how much time, effort or resources we invest in attempting to understand the brain and how it works, it remains elusive and daunting, which is perhaps why it has become the object of such attention. As has been aptly observed in an accompanying essay, it was Albert Einstein who noted: "The most beautiful thing we can experience is the mysterious. It is the true source of all art and science."

The brain is the great and universal enigma—one of the most daunting frontiers in the world of science. You will see in this issue that writers are wrestling with and capturing the mystery of the brain from a variety of points of view—from the impact of drugs to that of trauma and disease. Throughout the 1990s, that period referred to by the National Institutes of Mental Health as "the decade of the brain," scientists have unveiled a great deal of information leading to significant insight about the brain and how it works. As the decade ends, however, they are also beginning to understand how much more they need to know.

This is not only a scientific conundrum; what is observed under a microscope and by MRI (magnetic resonance imaging) significantly affects human beings in a number of different areas. The descriptions of attempting to live normally with a damaged brain by Marilyn A. Gelman and Floyd Skloot, and a brain affected by drugs, by Megan Foss and Greg Bottoms, are dramatic and touching illustrations of the complications and transformations to life when the brain is affected even ever so slightly and subtly. Three scientists are also represented in this issue: Ronald Pies and David Goldblatt, both physicians, as well as James Glanz, a writer for Science magazine.

Although high-quality creative nonfiction is always three-dimensional in scope, this issue expands the content and spirit of the genre by adding a fourth realm. In collaboration with the Pittsburgh Center for the Arts (PCA), one of the premier artistic institutions in the country, we have also captured the mystery of the brain in the way it best deserves—through creative depictions by some of the world's finest artists. In fact, this issue came about because of the creative vision of the PCA; curator Vicky Clark and director Laura Willumsen, working with exhibition curator Suzanne Ramljak, have scheduled an exhibit they have called "Romancing the Brain."

I was privileged to see slides of some of the works of art—creations of fascination and beauty. Our collaboration began at that moment: Creative Nonfiction would offer a cash prize of $500 for the best essay about some aspect of the brain (awarded to Skloot for "Gray Area: Thinking With a Damaged Brain") and devote an entire issue to essays which probe and explore the subject. The PCA would design its catalog to fit our journal and bind it in, adding an arresting, additional dimension to both the PCA exhibit and our issue. The PCA has also designed a program of educational explorations and activities with the help of the Pennsylvania Humanities Council, which will be conducted through the rest of the year. Pittsburgh's Carnegie Science Center has also become involved in this collaboration, and will be premiering "Gray Matters: The Brain Movie," an interactive brain installation this fall.

As noted in my editorial in Creative Nonfiction No. 12, responding with alacrity to natural and spontaneous personal and spiritual connections enables us to see art in a broader cultural context. This too, is the PCA's philosophy, according to Clark:

"I am presenting art of our times that provokes thought and gives us new insights and understandings by making connections to other ideas and disciplines. The brain show fits into this perfectly: We are dealing with a subject which has been touched upon by a variety of people. Each discipline has different tools, but the goal is the same: to understand an elusive object that is at the center of our being. As part of this investigation, our exhibit presents works of art that address the brain and attempt to come to an understanding of it, not only as a part of our body, but also as part of our culture."

Gray Area:
Thinking With a Damaged Brain
Floyd Skloot

I used to be able to think. My brain's circuits were all connected and I had spark, a quickness of mind that let me function well in the world. There were no problems with numbers or abstract reasoning; I could find the right word, could hold a thought in mind, match faces with names, converse coherently in crowded hallways, learn new tasks. I had a memory and an intuition that I could trust.

All that changed on December 7, 1988, when I contracted a virus that targeted my brain. A decade later, my cane and odd gait are the most visible evidence of damage. But most of the damage is hidden. My cerebral cortex, the gray matter that M.I.T. neuroscientist Steven Pinker likens to "a large sheet of two-dimensional tissue that has been wadded up to fit inside the spherical skull," has been riddled with tiny perforations. This sheet and the thinking it governs are now porous. Invisible to the naked eye, but readily seen through brain imaging technology, are areas of scar tissue that constrict blood flow. Anatomic holes, the lesions in my gray matter, appear as a scatter of white spots like bubbles or a ghostly pattern of potshots. Their effect is dramatic; I am like the brain-damaged patient described by neuroscientist V.S. Ramachandran in his book "Phantoms in the Brain": "Parts of her had forever vanished, lost in patches of permanently atrophied brain tissue." More hidden still are lesions in my Self, fissures in the thought process that result from this damage to my brain. When the brain changes, the mind changes—these lesions have altered who I am.

"When a disease process hits the brain," writes Dartmouth psychiatry professor Michael Gazzaniga in "Mind Matters," "the loss of nerve cells is easy to detect." Neurologists have a host of clinical tests that let them observe what a brain-damaged patient can and cannot do. They stroke his sole to test for a spinal reflex known as Babinski's sign or have him stand with feet together and eyes closed to see if the ability to maintain posture is compromised. They ask him to repeat a set of seven random digits forward and four in reverse order, to spell *world* backwards, to remember three specific words such as *barn* and *handsome* and *job* after a spell of unrelated conversation. A new laboratory technique, positron emission tomography, uses radioactively labeled oxygen or glucose that essentially lights up specific and different areas of the brain being used when a person speaks words or sees words or hears words, revealing the organic location for areas of behavioral malfunction. Another new technique, functional magnetic resonance imaging, allows increases in brain blood flow generated by certain actions to be measured. The resulting computer-generated pictures, eerily colorful relief maps of the brain's lunar topography, pinpoint hidden damage zones.

But I do not need a sophisticated and expensive high-tech test to know what my damaged brain looks like. People living with such injuries know intimately that things are awry. They see it in activities of daily living, in the way simple tasks become unmanageable. This morning, preparing oatmeal for my wife, Beverly, I carefully measured out one-third cup of oats and poured them onto the pan's lid rather than into the bowl. In its absence, a reliably functioning brain is something I can almost feel viscerally. The zip of connection, the shock of axon-to-axon information flow across a synapse, is not simply a textbook affair for me. Sometimes I see my brain as a scalded pudding, with fluky dark spots here and there through its dense layers and small scoops missing. Sometimes I see it as an eviscerated old TV console, wires all disconnected and misconnected, tubes blown, dust in the crevices.

Some of this personal, low-tech evidence is apparent in basic functions like walking, which for me requires intense concentration, as does maintaining balance and even breathing if I am tired. It is apparent in activities requiring the processing of certain fundamental information. For example, no matter how many times I have been shown how to do it, I cannot assemble our vacuum cleaner or our poultry shears or the attachments for our hand-cranked pasta maker. At my writing desk, I finish a note and place the pen in my half-full mug of tea rather than in its holder, which quite obviously teems with other pens. I struggle to figure out how a pillow goes into a pillowcase. I cannot properly adjust Beverly's stereo receiver in order to listen to the radio; it has been and remains useful to me only in its present setting as a CD player. These are all public, easily discernible malfunctions.

However, it is in the utterly private sphere that I most acutely experience how changed I am. Ramachandran compares this to harboring a zombie, playing host to a completely nonconscious being somewhere inside yourself. For me, being brain-damaged also has a physical, conscious component. Alone with my ideas and dreams and feelings, turned inward by the isolation and timelessness of chronic illness, I face a kind of ongoing mental vertigo in which thoughts teeter and topple into those fissures of cognition I mentioned earlier. I lose my way. I spend a lot of time staring into space, probably with my jaw drooping, as my concentration fragments and my focus dissolves. Thought itself has become a gray area, a matter of blurred edges and lost distinctions, with little that is sharp about it. This is not the way I used to be.

In their fascinating study, "Brain Repair," an international trio of neuroscientists—Donald G. Stein from America, Simon Brailowsky from Mexico and Bruno Will from France—report that after injury "both cortical and subcortical structures undergo dramatic changes in the pattern of blood flow and neural activity, even those structures that do not appear to be directly or primarily connected with the zone of injury." From this observation, they conclude that "the entire brain—not just the region around the area of damage—reorganizes in response to brain injury." The implications of this are staggering; my entire brain, the organ by which my very consciousness is controlled, was reorganized one day 10 years ago. I went to sleep *here* and woke up *there*; the place looked the same, but nothing in it worked the way it used to.

If Descartes was correct, and to Think is to Be, then what happens when I cannot think, or at least cannot think as I did, cannot think well enough to function in a job or in the world? Who am I?

You should hear me talk. I often come to a complete stop in midsentence, unable to find a word I need, and this silence is an apt reflection of the impulse blockage occurring in my brain. Sitting next to Beverly as she drives our pickup truck through Portland traffic at 6 p.m., I say, "We should have gone for pizza to avoid this blood ..." and cannot go on. I hear myself; I know I was about to say "blood tower traffic" instead of "rush hour traffic." Or I manifest staggered speech patterns—which feels like speaking with a limp—as I attempt to locate an elusive word. "I went to the ... *hospital* yesterday for some ... *tests* because my head ... *hurt.*" Or I blunder on, consumed by a feeling that something is going wrong, as when I put fresh grounds into the empty carafe instead of the filter basket on my coffee maker, put eye drops in my nose or spray the cleaning mist into my face instead of onto the shower walls. So at the dinner table I might say "Pass the sawdust" instead of "Pass the rice," knowing even as it happens that I am saying something inappropriate. I might start a conversation about "Winston Salem's new CD" instead of Wynton Marsalis' or announce that "the shore is breaking" when I mean to say "the shower is leaking." There is nothing smooth or unified anymore about the process by which I communicate; it is disintegrated and unpredictably awkward. My brain has suddenly become like an old man's. Neurologist David Goldblatt has developed a table which correlates cognitive decline in age-associated memory impairment and traumatic brain injury, and the parallels are remarkable. Not gradually, the way such changes occur naturally, but overnight, I was geezered.

It is not just about words. I am also *dyscalculic*, struggling with the math required to halve a recipe or to figure out how many more pages are left in a book I'm reading. If we are on East 82nd and Third Avenue in Manhattan, staying with my childhood friend Larry Salander for the week, it is very difficult for me to compute how far away the Gotham Book Mart is over on West 47th between Fifth and Sixth, though I spent much of my childhood in the city.

Because it is a place where I still try to operate normally, the kitchen is an ideal neurological observatory. After putting the leftover chicken in a plastic bag, I stick it back in the oven instead of the refrigerator. I put the freshly cleaned pan in the refrigerator, which is how I figure out that I must have put the chicken someplace else because it's missing. I pick up a chef's knife by its blade. I cut off an eighth of a giant white onion and then try to stuff the remainder into a recycled 16-ounce yogurt container that might just hold the small portion I set aside. I assemble ingredients for a vinaigrette dressing, pouring the oil into an old olive jar, adding balsamic vinegar, mustard, a touch of fresh lemon juice and spices. Then I screw the lid on upside-down and shake vigorously, spewing the contents everywhere. I stack the newspaper in the wood stove for recycling. I walk the garbage up our 200-yard-long driveway and try to put it in the mailbox instead of the trash container.

At home is one thing; when I perform these gaffes in public, the effect is often humiliating. I can be a spectacle. In a music store last fall, I was seeking an instruction book for Beverly, who wanted to relearn how to play her old recorder. She informed me that there were several kinds of recorders; it was important to buy exactly the right category of book since instructions for a soprano recorder would do her no good while learning on an alto. I made my way up to the counter and nodded when the saleswoman asked what I wanted. Nothing came out of my mouth, but I did manage to gesture over my right shoulder like an umpire signaling an out. I knew I was in trouble, but forged ahead anyway, saying, "Where are the books for sombrero reporters?" Last summer in Manhattan, I routinely exited the subway stations and led Beverly in the wrong direction, no matter which way we intended to go. She kept saying things like, "I think west is *that* way, sweetie," while I confidently and mistakenly headed east, into the glare of the morning sun, or, "Isn't that the river?" as I led her away from our riverside destination. Last week, in downtown Portland on a warm November morning, I stopped at the corner of 10th and Burnside, one of the busiest crossings in the city, carefully checked the traffic light (red) and the traffic lanes (bus coming), and started to walk into the street. A muttering transient standing beside me on his way to Powell's Books, where he was going to trade in his overnight haul of tomes for cash, grabbed my shoulder just in time.

At home or not at home, it ultimately makes no difference. The sensation of *dysfunctional mentation* is like being caught in a spiral of lostness. Outside the house, I operate with sporadic success, often not knowing where I am or where I'm going or what I'm doing. Inside the house, the same feelings often apply and I find myself standing at the top of the staircase wondering why I am going down. Even inside my head there is a feeling of being lost, thoughts that go nowhere, emptiness where I expect to find words or ideas, dreams I never remember.

Back in the fall, when it was Beverly's birthday, at least I did remember to go to the music store. More often, I forget what I am after within seconds of beginning the search. As she gets dressed for work, Beverly will tell me what she wants packed for lunch and I will forget her menu by the time I get up the 14 stairs. Now I write her order down like a waiter. Sometimes I think I should carry a pen at all times. In the midst of preparing a salad, I stop to walk the four paces over to the little desk where we keep our shopping list and forget "tomatoes" by the time I get there. So I should also have paper handy everywhere. Between looking up a phone number and dialing it, I forget the sequence. I need the whole phone book on my speed-dial system.

Though they appear without warning, these snafus are no longer strange to me. I know where they come from. As Dr. Richard M. Restak notes in "The Modular Brain," "A common error frequently resulting from brain damage involves producing a semantically related word instead of the correct response." But these paraphasias and neologisms, my *expressive aphasias*, and my dyscalculas and my failures to process—the rapids of confusion through which I feel myself flailing—though common for me and others with brain damage, are more than symptoms to me. They are also more than what neurologists like to call *deficits*, the word of choice when describing impairment or incapacity of neurological function, as Oliver Sacks explains in his introduction to "The Man Who Mistook His Wife for a Hat." These "deficits" have been incorporated into my very being, my consciousness. They are now part of my repertoire. Deficits imply losses; I have to know how to see them as gains.

Practitioners of neuroscience call the damage caused by trauma, stroke or disease "an insult to the brain." So pervasive is this language that the states of Georgia, Kentucky and Minnesota, among others, incorporate the phrase "insult to the brain" in their statutory definitions of traumatic brain injury for disability determinations. Such insults, according to the Brain Injury Association of Utah, "may produce a diminished or altered state of consciousness, which results in an impairment of cognitive abilities or physical functioning." The death of one Miles Dethmuffen, front man and founding member of the Boston rock band Dethmuffen, was attributed in news reports to "an alcoholic insult to the brain." The language used is so cool. There is this sentence from the Web site NeuroAdvance.com: "When there is an insult to the brain, some of the cells die." Yes.

Insult is an exquisitely zany word for the catastrophic neurological event it is meant to describe. In current usage, of course, insult generally refers to an offensive remark or action, an affront, a violation of mannerly conduct. To insult is to treat with gross insensitivity, insolence or contemptuous rudeness. The medical meaning, however, as with so many other medical words and phrases, is different, older, linked to a sense of the word that is some two or three centuries out of date. *Insult* comes from the Latin compound verb *insultare*, which means "to jump on" and is also the root word for *assault* and *assail*. It's a word that connotes aggressive physical abuse, an attack. Originally, it suggested leaping upon the prostrate body of a foe, which may be how its link to contemptuous action was forged.

Though "an insult to the brain" (a blow to the head, a metal shard through the skull, a stroke, a viral "attack") is a kind of assault, I am curious about the way *contempt* has found its way into the matter. Contempt was always part of the meaning of insult and now it is primary to the meaning. Certainly a virus is not acting contemptuously when it targets the brain; neither is the pavement nor steering wheel nor falling wrench nor clot of blood nor most other agents of "insult." But I think society at large, medical scientists, insurers, legislators, and the person on the street do feel a kind of contempt for the brain damaged with their comical way of walking, their odd patterns of speech or ways in which neurological damage is expressed, their apparent stupidity, their abnormality. The damage done to a brain seems to evoke disdain in those who observe it and shame or disgrace in those who experience it.

Poet Peter Davison has noticed the resonant irony of the phrase "an insult to the brain" and made use of it in his poem "The Obituary Writer." Thinking about the suicide of John Berryman, the heavily addicted poet whose long-expected death in 1972 followed years of public behavior symptomatic of brain damage, Davison writes that "his hullabaloos/of falling-down drunkenness were an insult to the brain." In this poem, toying with the meaning of the phrase, Davison suggests that Berryman's drinking may have been an insult to his brain, technically speaking, but that watching him was, for a friend, another kind of brain insult. He has grasped the fatuousness of the phrase as a medical term, its inherent judgment of contempt, and made use of it for its poetic ambiguity.

But I have become enamored of the idea that my brain has been insulted by a virus. I use it as motivation. There is a long tradition of avenging insults through duels or counter-insults, through litigation, through the public humiliation of the original insult. So I write. I avenge myself on an insult that was meant, it feels, to silence me by compromising my word-finding capacity, my ability to concentrate and remember, to spell or conceptualize, to express myself, to think.

The duel is fought over and over. I have developed certain habits that enable me to work—a team of seconds, to elaborate this metaphor of a duel. I must be willing to write slowly, to skip or leave blank spaces where I cannot find words that I seek, compose in fragments and without an overall ordering principle or imposed form. I explore and make discoveries in my writing now, never quite sure where I am going, but willing to let things ride and discover later how they all fit together. Every time I finish an essay or poem or piece of fiction, it feels as though I have faced down the insult.

In his book "Creating Mind," Harvard neurobiologist John E. Dowling says "the cerebral cortex of the human brain, the seat of higher neural function—perception, memory, language, and intelligence—is far more developed than is the cerebral cortex of any other vertebrate." Our gray matter is what makes us human. Dowling goes on to say that "because of the added neural cells and cortical development in the human brain, new facets of mind emerge." Like the fractured facet of a gemstone or crystal, like a crack in the facet of a bone, a chipped facet of mind corrupts the whole, and this is what an insult to the brain does.

Though people long believed, with Aristotle, that the mind was located within the heart, the link between brain and mind is by now a basic fact of cognitive science. Like countless others, I am living proof of it. Indeed, it is by studying the behavior of brain-damaged patients like me that medical science first learned, for example, that the brain is modular, with specific areas responsible for specific functions, or that functions on one side of the body are controlled by areas on the opposite side of the brain. "The odd behavior of these patients," says Ramachandran, speaking of the brain-damaged, "can help us solve the mystery of how various parts of the brain create a useful representation of the external world and generate the illusion of 'self' that endures in space and time." Unfortunately, there is ample opportunity to observe this in action since, according to the Brain Injury Association, more than two million Americans suffer traumatic brain injury every year, a total that does not include damage by disease.

"Change the brain, change the person," says Restak in "The Modular Brain." But how, exactly? No one has yet explained the way a brain produces what we think of as consciousness. How does the firing of electrical impulse across a synapse produce love, math, nightmare, theology, appetite? Stated more traditionally, how do brain and mind interact? Bookstore shelves are now filled with books, like Steven Pinker's brilliant 1997 study, "How the Mind Works," which attempt to explain how a 3-pound organ the consistency of Jell-O makes us see, think, feel, choose, and act. "The mind is not the brain," Pinker says, "but what the brain does."

And what the brain does, according to Pinker, "is information processing, or computation." We think we think with our brain. But in doing its job of creating consciousness, the brain actually relies upon a vast network of systems and is connected to everything—eyes, ears, skin, limbs, nerves. As Dowling so dourly puts it, our mental function, our mind—memory, feelings, emotions, awareness, understanding, creativity—"is an emergent property of brain function." In other words, "What we refer to as mind is a natural consequence of complex and higher neural processing."

The key word is *processing*. We actually think with our whole body. The brain, however, takes what is shipped to it, crunches the data, and sends back instructions. It converts; it generates results. Or, when damaged, does not. There is nothing wrong with my sensory receptors, for instance. I see quite well. I can hear and smell; my speech mechanisms (tongue, lips, nerves) are intact. My skin remains sensitive. But it's in putting things together that I fail. Messages get garbled, blocked, missed. There is, it sometimes seems, a lot of static when I try to think, and this is the gray area where nothing is clear any longer.

Neurons, the brain's nerve cells, are designed to process information. They "receive, integrate and transmit," as Dowling says, receiving input from dendrites and transmitting output along axons, sending messages to one another across chemical passages called *synapses*. When there are lesions like the ones that riddle my gray matter, processing is compromised. Not only that, certain cells have simply died and with them the receiving, integrating and transmitting functions they performed.

My mind does not make connections because, in essence, some of my brain's connectors have been broken or frayed. I simply have less to work with and it is no surprise that my IQ dropped measurably in the aftermath of my illness. Failing to make connections, on both the physical and metaphysical levels, is distressing. It is very difficult for me to free-associate; my stream of consciousness does not absorb runoff or feeder streams well, but rushes headlong instead. Mental activity that should follow a distinct pattern does not and, indeed, I experience my thought process as subject to random misfirings. I do not feel in control of my intelligence. Saying "Pass me the tracks" when I intended to say "Pass me the gravy" is a nifty example. Was it because *gravy* sounds like *grooves* which led to tracks or because my tendency to spill gravy leaves tracks on my clothes? A misfire, a glitch in the gray area that thought has become for me, and as a result my ability to express myself is compromised. My very nature seems to have altered.

I am also easily overloaded. I cannot read the menu or converse in a crowded, noisy restaurant. I get exhausted at Portland Trailblazers basketball games, with all the visual and aural imagery, all the manufactured commotion, so I stopped going nine years ago. My hands are scarred from burns and cuts that occurred when I tried to cook and converse at the same time. I cannot drive in traffic, especially in our standard transmission pickup truck. I cannot talk about, say, the fiction of Thomas Hardy while I drive; I need to be given directions in small doses rather than all at once, and need those directions to be given precisely at the time I must make the required turn. This is, as Restak explains, because driving and talking about Hardy, or driving and processing information about where to turn, are handled by different parts of the brain and my brain's parts have trouble working together.

I used to write accompanied by soft jazz, but now the least pattern of noises distracts me and shatters concentration. My entire writing process, in fact, has been transformed as I learned to work with my newly configured brain and its strange snags. I have become an avid note taker, a jotter of random thoughts that might or might not find their way together or amount to anything, a writer of bursts instead of steady work. A slight interruption—the movement of my cat across my window view, the call of a hawk, a spell of coughing—will not just make me lose my train of thought, it will leave me at the station for the rest of the day.

I have just finished reading a new book about Muhammad Ali, "King of the World," by David Remnick. I anticipated identifying a bit with Ali, now suffering from Parkinson's disease, who shows so strikingly what brain damage can do, stripped as he is of so many of the functions—speech, movement, spontaneity—that once characterized him. But it was reading about Floyd Patterson that got me.

Patterson was a childhood hero of mine. Not only did we share a rare first name, we lived in neighboring towns—he was in Rockville Center, on Long Island, while I was five minutes away in Long Beach, just across the bridge. I was 9 when he beat Archie Moore to take the heavyweight championship belt, almost 12 when he lost it to Ingemar Johannson and almost 13 when he so memorably won it back. The image of Johannson's left leg quivering as he lay unconscious on the mat is one of those vivid memories that endures (because, apparently, it is stored in a different part of the brain than other, less momentous memories). That Floyd, like me, was small of stature in his world, was shy and vulnerable, and I was powerfully drawn to him.

During his 64 professional fights, his long amateur career, his many rounds of sparring to prepare for fights, Patterson absorbed a tremendous amount of damage to his brain. Now in his 60s, his ability to think is devastated. Testifying in court earlier this year in his capacity as head of the New York State Athletic Commission, Patterson "generally seemed lost," according to Remnick. He could not remember the names of his fellow commissioners, his phone number or secretary's name or lawyer's name. He could not remember the year of his greatest fight, against Archie Moore, or "the most basic rules of boxing (the size of the ring, the number of rounds in a championship fight)." He kept responding to questions by saying, "It's hard to think when I'm tired."

Finally, admitting "I'm lost," he said, "Sometimes I can't even remember my wife's name, and I've been married 32, 33 years." He added again that it was hard for him to think when he was tired. "Sometimes, I can't even remember my own name."

People often ask if I will ever "get better." In part, I think what they wonder about is whether the brain can heal itself. Will I be able, either suddenly or gradually, to think as I once did? Will I toss aside the cane, be free of symptoms, have all the functions governed by my brain restored to smooth service, rejoin the world of work and long-distance running? The question tends to catch me by surprise because I believe I have stopped asking it myself.

The conventional wisdom has long been that brains do not repair themselves. Other body tissue, other kinds of cells, are replaced after damage, but "When brain cells are lost because of injury or disease," Dowling wrote as recently as 1998, "they are not replaced." We have, he says, as many brain cells at age one as we will ever have. This has been a fundamental tenet of neuroscience, yet it has also long been clear that people do recover—fully or in part—from brain injury. Some stroke victims relearn to walk and talk; feeling returns in once numb limbs. Children—especially children—recover and show no lasting ill effects from catastrophic injuries or coma-inducing bouts of meningitis.

So brain cells do not get replaced or repaired, but brain-damaged people occasionally do regain function. In a sense, then, the brain heals, but its cells do not.

In "Confronting Traumatic Brain Injury," Texas bioethicist William J. Winslade says, "Scientists still don't understand how the brain heals itself." He adds that although "Until recently, neuroscientists thought that much of the loss of capabilities due to brain damage was irreversible," patients recover spontaneously and rehabilitation programs "can restore cognitive and functional skills and emotional and experiential capacity, at least in part."

There are in general five theories about the way people might recover function lost to brain damage. One suggests that we do not need all of our brain because we only use a small part of it to function. Another is that some brain tissue can be made to take over functions lost to damage elsewhere. Connected to this is the idea that the brain has a backup mechanism in place allowing cells to take over like understudies. Rehabilitation can teach people new ways to perform some old tasks, bypassing the whole damaged area altogether. And finally, there is the theory that in time, and after the chemical shock of the original injury, things return to normal and we just get better.

It is probably true that, for me, a few of these healing phenomena have taken place. I have, for instance, gotten more adept at tying my shoes, taking a shower, driving for short periods. With careful preparation, I can appear in public to read from my work or attend a party. I have developed techniques to slow down my interactions with people or to incorporate my mistakes into a longer-term process of communications or composition. I may not be very good in spontaneous situations, but given time to craft my responses I can sometimes do well. But I still can't think.

A recent development promises to up the ante in the game of recovery from brain damage. The New York Times reported in October of 1998, that "Adult humans can generate new brain cells." A team at the Salk Institute for Biological Studies in La Jolla, California, observed new growth in cells of the hippocampus, which controls learning and memory in the brain. The team's leader, Dr. Fred Gage, expressed the usual cautions; more time is needed to "learn whether new cell creation can be put to work" and under what conditions. But the findings were deemed both "interesting" and "important."

There is only one sensible response to news like this. It has no personal meaning to me. Clinical use of the finding lies so far in the future as to be useless, even if regenerating cells could restore my lost functions. Best not to think about this sort of thing.

Because, in fact, the question of whether I will ever get better is meaningless. To continue looking outside for a cure, a "magic bullet," some combination of therapies and treatments and chemicals to restore what I have lost is to miss the point altogether. Certainly if a safe, effective way existed to resurrect dead cells, or generate replacements, and if this somehow guaranteed that I would flash back or flash forward to "be the person I was," it would be tempting to try.

But how would that be? Would the memories that have vanished reappear? Not likely. Would I be like the man, blind for decades, who had sight restored and could not handle the experience of vision, could not make sense of a world he could see? I am, in fact, who I am now. I have changed. I have learned to live and live richly as I am now. Slowed down, softer, more heedful of all that I see and hear and feel, more removed from the hubbub, more internal. I have made certain decisions, such as moving from the city to a remote rural hilltop in the middle of acres of forest, that have turned out to be good for my health and even my soul. I have gained the love of a woman who knew me before I got sick and likes me much better now. Certainly I want to be well. I miss being able to think clearly and sharply, to function in the world, to move with grace. I miss the feeling of coherence or integrity that comes with a functional brain. I feel old before my time.

In many important respects, then, I have already gotten better. I continue to learn new ways of living with a damaged brain. I continue to make progress, to avenge the insult, to see my way around the gray area. But no, I am not going to be the man I was. In this, I am hardly alone.

Floyd Skloot's essays have appeared in The American Scholar, Boulevard, Southwest Review, Antioch Review, Gettysburg Review, Commonweal, Threepenny Review, Witness and many other magazines. His first collection of essays, "The Night Side," was published by Story Line Press and named one of the best books of the season by New Age Journal. Skloot has also published three novels and two books of poetry.

Perspectivo Scientifico
or, Where the Rays Convene, I Fix a Point
Susan L. Rose

Go *to the pillar separating the medieval section of the museum from the gallery of Renaissance paintings and stop. If you listen carefully—very carefully—you can hear a quiet gasp as the medieval painter, after a hundred years of trial and error (give or take a few), finally grasps the notion of perspective and stumbles into enlightenment.*

But we. We gasp when we finally stumble and see that we don't really have true perspective.

When I was in high school, I had a gigantic acacia tree pressing against the windowpanes of my second-story, corner bedroom. In January the tree would pop into flower, like kernels of corn in a pale green pan. They grew and grew until there was no more green to see. Just fragrant, joyful yellow outside my sanctuary.

But it was a dirty tree. The dried flowers tumbled to the ground in handfuls and stuck like fuzz to the bottoms of your shoes. The thin, brown seed pods twisted, split and shattered their seed on the ground. And then hundreds of tiny delicate trees sprang up like weeds.

"It's got to go," my mother said. "I can't take the mess. And it blocks the view." One day it was gone.

In the morning the sun rose up over the freeway, cleared the roofs of the neighboring houses and the telephone wires and came blaring into the room. My mother pushed the bedroom door.

"Now, isn't all this sunshine nice?" she declared.

I crossed my eyes at her and growled. My tree was gone: another reason to leave.

European painting of the medieval period is characterized by flatness. Everything that needs revealing is on the painting's surface. Past events are portrayed in hazes of activity on the sky while the present moment of the painting looms large on the middle ground of the panel. Future conditionals cringe below the dark line of terra firma.

This two-dimensional schematic for painting suits the hierarchy of the medieval church: The world is flat, God is above, Purgatory and Hell below, and there are only two possible endings to a man's life. Like childhood, it is a simplicity that serves well. But unlike the Byzantine, its flatness is striving to go somewhere. Striving for a new alignment with the stars and the sky, a new horizon.

In college, supposedly, Americans broaden their horizons. Get exposed to new points of view. Learn to be independent thinkers. In fact, maybe all that happens is the tree is cut down so that we can look out the window for the first time. And then, depending on our personalities and families, we head back to our familiar horizons and to a chosen course, or we fall for the allure of the distant horizon.

After college I gathered my little money and went off to visit relatives living on the distant horizons. I imposed on addresses, smelled the strange smells in their kitchens, slept under strange blankets and did my best to utter strange words. Finally I ran out of addresses and the Joni Mitchell tape I played in my head was getting faint. Someone said, "Go visit my cousin in West Berlin." I packed my camera and notebook and was on the train the next day.

I ended up in a bullet-ridden, crumbling, 18th century plastered building on a gray cobblestone street, deadly in winter. The toilet was in a cubicle on the landing halfway down the stairway (or up, depending on where your apartment was). When I moved to an apartment with its own toilet, I had the view of a dark, inner third courtyard of a factory, cluttered with ash cans and cats, and one perennially dying tree.

I moved again and got my own cat. My fifth-floor balcony looked down at a blanket-sized patch of garden with a dusty broken brick wall. On the other side of the wall were the deserted wilds of a wide strip of abandoned S-Bahn terrain. There was a large gap in the fence and I took long walks there. In the afternoons I explained the present participle. At night I got high on Pilsner and schnapps and discussions of the social construction of reality. One day I fell asleep in the middle of a private lesson. Mortified, I went home to figure out on whose horizon I'd been.

In the afternoon of the 14th century the medieval painter sits back from his work and realizes that what he is painting is not what he is seeing. That there is a material world with its own horizons and natural laws. He decides to impose a grid of orthogonals on the surface of his painting, as if to make a doorway through which he can pass into the three-dimensional space he senses beyond. He uses the flat plane of his grid to attenuate objects. But the effect is not right. The horizon has too many points and the side angles extend in too many directions. Things are still floating and he is still learning to see.

I was in graduate school, working on my future, convinced I would never go back to Europe, taking a huge bite of my sprout-and-cream-cheese sandwich when an acquaintance of a fellow student walked up. He gave me a coincidental smile while he talked to the fellow student, and then he left. But we ran into each other again and again until the coincidental smiles became smiles of complicity and the acquaintance of an acquaintance became a point of reference. Life can be that way.

He was, it turned out, visiting from his tiny, picturesquely wealthy, pastorally beautiful, European country. And it would soon be time to go back. I couldn't fathom life without him any more than I could fathom it with him. He, on the other hand, had a plan. So I dumped mine and we married.

But I was sure I was returning to a familiar horizon, just with more perspective. We found a very modern apartment and moved in. This time I had a modern view, a dishwasher and a bathroom-and-a-half.

I went shopping every day with a willow basket slung over my arm and did my wash on Mondays. I learned to put the fork in my left hand and the knife in my right and to shake hands or kiss cheeks whenever I met someone I knew. I ate *steak de cheval* and overcooked vegetables. I learned to take chrysanthemums and heather to the graves on All Saints' Day. And finally I learned to push a baby carriage, make ratatouille for lunch and ignore the view out my modern kitchen window.

As the 14th century is drawing to a close, the painters say, "Well, if we can't get this attenuation part right, at least we can create the illusion of perspective." They want to imitate the diffusion of light as it recedes toward the horizon on an early spring evening when the sky is smoldering with blue and black rain clouds over the golden-green fields. Atmospheric perspective requires complex color mixing. But there is a problem: The tempera paint is drying too quickly. Adding more egg yolk doesn't help. Oil paint needs to be discovered.

Jan van Eyck, alive in 1390 and dead by 1440, has been credited with the invention of oil paint. I'm sure it was a propitious moment of coincidence, the kind that mark all important changes in point of view. Probably his wife (for all painters were men in those days) brusquely set down the oil lamp one night, angry that it was she who had the flu and still had to put all the children to bed. The oil sloshed irritably onto his palette, brilliant with splotches of tempera drying quicker than he could get it onto his panel. "Watch what you're doing, woman!" he cried, but she was gone. The oil slid serpentinely around the eggy patches and caught bits of the scattered pigment dust, and held them suspended. Fascinated, he forgot about his wife with the flu and his 11 children.

In my new country, I met a beautiful but—as it turned out—always unhappy friend. Even though two towns separated us, we were neighbors because we were surrounded by a strange language. One day I visited her. She was in the hospital again, doing tests, but I never quite got what was wrong.

This time her room was on the 12th floor, with an expansive view of a broad winter flatland. On it, in the curve of a river wending along a forest-topped sandstone cliff, stretched the red-tiled roofs of a brown and gray European town. Cathedral towers reached up, marking the long bar of snow-covered Alps forming the horizon.

"What a view," I sighed, my eyes lingering on the horizon the way they linger over desserts.

"I don't want a view," she sighed weakly, "I want someone to save me." I looked at her wan face. "I'm sorry," I said, "I don't even know how to save myself."

I said goodbye, picked up the kids and went home to my European efficiency kitchen. The carrots I'd bought at the market that morning were still wrapped in newspaper by the sink, the epitome of

European charm. I turned and looked out the window.

I saw a flat gray apartment building behind an empty playground (the mothers didn't come out till after nap time). A pine tree leaned weakly over the desolate sandbox. An old woman, bundled in a thick coat and stockings, pulled a shopping trolley into the high-rise. The pale sun squeezed through a passing hole in the trundling clouds as if it were stubbornly heading out regardless of the weather.

The next morning I looked at my husband in surprise and announced, "I'm going home."

My husband stared at me, his thick slice of bread spread with currant jam in midair to his mouth.

"Why?" he asked, stupefied.

"It's the view," I said, shaking my head. "I just can't stand the view."

Every view implies a vanishing point. A vanishing point, at its most abstract, is nothing more than points converging at infinity on an ideal horizon, one that we have created for ourselves. Mathematically speaking, it is the fixed point that forms the axis of two or more coordinates. Picturesquely, it is a hole that pierces the horizon. The piercing that gives it perspective.

Our painter, sitting on the threshold of the Renaissance in his dirty smock, stares piercingly out his atelier window. He does not yet quite know what is missing in his painting. He senses the narrowing of energy straining toward the horizon, he has made a grid, his passageway, but he is still not satisfied. His view keeps shifting. Until he suddenly realizes the absolute importance of himself, that one spot in the world where he is sitting and looking, mixing pigments and thinking about God and the world.

I flew home with just the children. The children said, "This isn't home."

"Enjoy it," I answered. "It'll give you a new point of view."

But I wasn't feeling very much at home in a place I was used to calling home. I looked around for the horizon. A steady stream of cars threaded its tangled way over the hills and choked the view. Friends dashed in and out, leaving hurried messages of no importance. Houses spread across every hill and ridge. Homeless lined some streets, while jostling jeeps studded every parking lot. Had it been so long? In the stores I studied rows of labels and in the end bought only one box of cereal, one bag of bagels and one jar of peanut butter.

I went to the bookstores. I wandered the malls. I had long telephone conversations with kind friends and wrote long letters to my husband. Negotiation, whether with other people or with oneself, is a tricky thing. It requires a certain flexibility, and yet an unfailing sense of where one is in the world. It requires patience and understanding.

The grid, the point of reference, the oil paint, the horizon and the morning of the 15th century. The sky is taking on new dimensions; the world is opening up. The life hereafter is slinking back under the pews of the cathedral and minds are travelling.

In Florence, Filipo Brunelleschi is fascinated by the idea of representing mathematical relationships in space. He convinces his friend Donatello, the painter, to go with him to Rome to do some measuring. Every day for a whole year he measures while Donatello paints. By the time he returns to Florence, he's figured out the architecture of proportion and relation. With certainty, he publishes "Construzione Legittima," but linear perspective remains abstract.

"This is not enough," thinks Leon Battista Alberti as he sits on his vine-covered terrace one afternoon in 1435. "We have enough intelligence to deal with this insight in a concrete way." He takes up his metal pen nib and homemade ink and begins to write: The view we see is constructed of a pyramid of light. The base of the pyramid is the surface we see, while the apex of the pyramid, where all rays of light convene, rests within us. "Post haec unicum punctum" … To find true perspective, I choose a single point where the rays of light meet for me, and I fix that point.[1]

"De Pittura" travels quickly through Italy and Germany, to Flanders and Holland. It is met with excitement, astonishment and joy. The secret of true perspective is so simple: You need a fixed point of reference (the viewer or yourself), a horizon and a point on the horizon toward which imaginary lines extend beyond the painting into infinity.

It seems obvious, now, from where we sit in history; every schoolchild learns to draw perspective. But back then it took over a hundred years to figure out the necessity of using the self as a systematic reference point.

---

1. "de Pictura" L.B, Alberti, 1435; Book I, section 7.

One day I took my children to the beach. While they climbed a rock I stared at the low, sparkling-green wall of the Pacific. I pressed my bare feet hard against the cool sand. I breathed deeply, thinking about orthogonals and wondering if square miles of openness could constitute a grid. Sunlight glittered in tiny points across the water until one in particular, right on the edge of the horizon, where the ocean reaches the sky, caught my eye.

I stared at it so hard that it suddenly pierced the horizon and I sailed on past miles of islands to continents of land filled with billions of people, all living and breathing and doing the million different things that they do in their millions of different ways. Millions of straggly roosters crowed while millions of dogs of every color barked at the edge of many jungles.

A seagull landed three feet away and eyed me crossly. I was obviously disturbing his view. I looked back at the sea. I understood—the view is not what is in front of our eyes, but the architecture we give to that view. I had left home without knowing where my reference point was, had put up a grid without knowing where my vanishing point was. Why should I blame someone else for my ignorance of perspective?

Without perspective, where do we go in life, I ask myself, sipping the last of my California Zinfandel as I sit on the enormous yellow flowered sofa I bought last week. I look out the window. I like this new house. My husband has chosen well: It has many windows.

A pristine glide of pasture slides down to a wide, sheltering tile roof on an old Swiss farmhouse before slipping gracefully up beyond the dark green woods (where mist rises on November days), past the tiny steepled village on its way up the foothill, and on to the perfectly formed silhouette of the Alps. Snow-covered Alps. Breathlessly cold and crisp on a clear day.

They rear up into the sky and part. When I look out the window, I can see Hannibal and his elephants floating over the pass. Back march Swiss merchant soldiers. Up struggle factory workers. Back grind trucks loaded with Mercedes and BMWs. Light quivers behind the glacial slopes. Warm fragrant winds, heavy with salty moisture, waft up and are sometimes caught by the cold fists of the north, and then they cry. But when they pass through, the frigid northern farmland swells and blossoms. Why hadn't I seen this before? Was I too busy blaming?

A hundred years after Alberti, Albrecht Dürer erected free-standing screens in front of objects and pulled strings taut between them and his drawing paper in order to show true scientific perspective. He did not call it art; he called it science. Another hundred years and Abraham Bosse, taken by the idea of mathematics in the service of vision and art, proposes an even simpler, portable method for seeing perspective. The visual pyramid—a kind of hand-held box like a slide viewer—allows potential perspecteurs to wander at will. Whenever they wish, they can stop, hold the visual pyramid up to their eye. The sides of the pyramid form a natural glide to the apex, the point toward which lines convene. Wherever I go, I can fix a point. Such clear constraints provide the basis for a new kind of liberty.

Perspective pointed the way for the camera obscura, *a simple, closed box with a hole that allowed only a selection of reflected light to enter. It must have been the painter's great-great grandson who, tired of the easel and looking at his own thumb stretched out against the horizon, said, "I need a more objective point of view." But imagine, without pinning down one's own point of view, the camera would not have been possible.*

"So, how's your view," I ask my always beautiful friend. She's over having lunch, but it doesn't please her, I can tell. I have forgotten how to cook.

"Everything is the same," she says, pushing back her chair. Her eyes roll sardonically. "I can't take it anymore," she whispers. "See you later," she says as she goes out the door. I know now what she is going to do. She can afford the quick fix.

"Wait!" I want to shout. "Don't go! Try this *pyramida perspectiva!* It makes things easier. *Post haec unicum punctum!*"

If half of life is chosen, and half is accidental, is the horizon the line between the two? But she's already left and, in fact, there is no scientific device to help us find perspective in this post-modern life.

I return to my sofa with a sigh. Behind the granite blue and white mountains stretched across the horizon like a birthday-card streamer, I see clouds pushing up from the south. I can live with this view. I have chosen it. And perhaps it has chosen me. It changes every day—a misplaced word, a meaningful gesture—but I know where I am.

And there, between two peaks, where I have made the point that pierces my horizon, I draw lines of convergence.

Selection and relation. Perspectivo scientifico.

Birds take flight,
The clouds drain from the sky
I and the mountain sit together
until only the mountain remains.

—purloined and adapted from Li Po

Susan L. Rose *is a writer, editor and translator working near Fribourg, Switzerland. Her most recent work is an adventure novel for middle-grade readers.*

SUBSCRIBE

YES! I want to read CREATIVE NONFICTION.

- ❑ **Save 36% off the cover price! 1 year—$22⁵⁰**
- ❑ **Save 50% off newsstand price! TWO YEARS—6 ISSUES FOR $35**

Name _____

Address _____

City _____

State _____ Zip _____

Daytime Phone ( ) _____

- ❑ **Payment enclosed** (payable to "Creative Nonfiction Foundation")   ❑ **Please bill me**
- ❑ **Contact me** about using CREATIVE NONFICTION as a course text
- ❑ **Charge my** ❑ Visa ❑ **Mastercard**   Expires _____

Card# _____   Signature X _____

Canadian rate: One year/$30, two year/$45. Other foreign: one year/$35, two year/$70. Remit in U.S. funds. Allow 4–6 weeks for delivery of first issue.

❖ CREATIVE NONFICTION ❖   3I9R

GIVE A GIFT

Great savings on gift subscriptions to CREATIVE NONFICTION.

First gift—$22⁵⁰ | **Each additional gift—Only $19⁹⁵!**
(Your own subscription counts as your first gift.)

Recipient's Name _____

Recipient's Address _____

City _____ State _____ Zip _____

Gift card from _____ Giver's Phone ( ) _____

Giver's Address _____

City _____ State _____ Zip _____

- ❑ **Payment enclosed** (payable to "Creative Nonfiction Foundation")   ❑ **Please bill me**
- ❑ **Charge my** ❑ Visa ❑ **Mastercard**   Expires _____

Card# _____   Signature X _____

Canadian rate: $30. Other foreign rates: $35. Remit in U.S. funds. Allow 4–6 weeks for delivery of first issue.
For multiple gift orders, please print clearly on a separate sheet of paper or call us at (412) 688-0304

❖ CREATIVE NONFICTION ❖   3I9RG

Order by phone (412) 688-0304 or FAX this form to (412) 683-9173

BUSINESS REPLY MAIL
FIRST CLASS MAIL   PERMIT NO. 17218-526   PITTSBURGH, PA

POSTAGE WILL BE PAID BY ADDRESSEE

CREATIVE NONFICTION
PO BOX 3000
DENVILLE NJ 07834-9259

NO POSTAGE
NECESSARY
IF MAILED
IN THE
UNITED STATES

BUSINESS REPLY MAIL
FIRST CLASS MAIL   PERMIT NO. 17218-526   PITTSBURGH, PA

POSTAGE WILL BE PAID BY ADDRESSEE

CREATIVE NONFICTION
PO BOX 3000
DENVILLE NJ 07834-9259

Not in Love With AAMI

David Goldblatt

Might as well begin with the latest one: This morning, walking the beagle and thinking how to start this article, I began to pass the springhouse (a little shed over a cinderblock tank at the top of our hill), which I rebuilt last year in preparation for piping water to the outbuilding where I have my office. Sparky, deep in his world of smells, was having his usual good time but—just back from a quick trip to San Diego and a long beach stroll that compared favorably with dogwalking in the chill of a January morning in upstate New York—I was not. I owed my stepson, Ricky, for his good care of my cats while Ann and I were away, but was wishing that my voluntary repayment had not taken the form of walking his dog for him. Hurrying as I was, I had already passed the springhouse before I stopped, recalling Ann's comment of the night before that it would be good to check the water level, now that the water project was nearing completion in a time of relative drought in our area. Maybe we'd get all through with the work, only to discover that the source was dry.

Hopping cautiously over the ice crust on the drainage ditch, I entered the woods, removed the access panel on the north side of the springhouse, lifted and set aside the screen that is supposed to keep mice and other small creatures from drowning in the water beneath, then found a pole, poked it through the surface ice, and ascertained that a recent heavy snow and subsequent thaw had indeed helped to raise the level of the water. Pleased with the information I had obtained, I put down the pole, replaced the panel, twisted the four pieces of hardware into place to hold it, recovered the dog's leash, and started down the hill.

Then I stopped, decided I had to go back to recheck, renegotiated the frozen ditch, reopened the panel, and, sure enough, found that I had not repositioned the varmint screen over the top of the holding tank. As I closed up the shed, I asked myself if I had now got everything right, and I wondered whether, in a few years, I might instead be asking questions like, "Now tell me, are you Ricky or Sparky?" And would I be addressing my question to my stepson or his dog? Or perhaps to a shed? I wasn't really ready to think about that, but I couldn't help it. I had a more general question on my mind that was shaping my thinking and is the subject of this essay: Does my age-associated memory impairment (AAMI) represent the insidious onset of Alzheimer's disease (AD), or is it something I can continue to live and function with? It is a question that many people ask in an aging America.

As a neurologist, I have tried in the past to answer that question for some of my patients from the physician's side of the desk. The case of "Mort" is one example. (Circumstances alter cases, and in this and other descriptions of persons in this essay, I have had to change names and occupations, but I have not otherwise created fiction.) Until his retirement, which had taken place a couple of years before he came to see me, Mort was an administrator at the hospital where I also worked. We knew each other casually, and I thought he always looked harried. This time, though, he admitted it. He wanted to know if he was becoming demented and, from experience, I knew that I could not just pat him on the head. Like medical students who must undergo a complete neurological examination before they can begin to believe that the muscle twitches that prevent them from concentrating on their studies are benign, and not the first sign of amyotrophic lateral sclerosis, people who come for reassurance about their subjective mental decline must also be put through their paces. This is the rule of thumb: If the patient is the one who made the appointment to complain about his memory, he is fine; if a family member made the appointment and brought the patient in, and the patient says he is fine, he isn't. But you can't reach either conclusion without examining the patient. Moreover, the rule works best when things have moved along. At the onset of dementia, insight may be retained. This poignant line appeared in a British medical journal, The Lancet, in an anonymous woman's essay on her father's progressive dementia:

"In that moment he knew for certain that he was losing his mind, and I think he knew as well as I did that he was losing it for ever."

He was 70, Mort said, and his mother had become demented in the 10-year course of Parkinson's disease. He was concerned about his tendency to lose a thought, especially when he was distracted. And he would often go somewhere in the house to get something, then stand there wondering what he had come for. Usually—not always—he could retrace his steps mentally and recover the lost plan. Sometimes, he woke up too late to the fact that he should be in a meeting or picking up a friend at the airport.

I did examine Mort, but it was his history that answered his question. From one full-time job he had gone to so many part-time jobs it was no wonder he was forgetting to keep appointments. He volunteered at the library, at the synagogue, at the town office, at the local newspaper. There were projects in various stages of completion. The list was so long I stopped writing (and now, of course, I can no longer remember what the items all were).

After my neurological examination, which showed none of the stigmata of parkinsonism or those that may accompany AD, multi-infarct dementia and other forms of cerebral vascular disease, or normal-pressure hydrocephalus, I gave Mort the Folstein/McHugh Mini-Mental State Examination (MMSE), the best known of the screening tests for dementia, which has been in use for nearly a quarter of a century. Neurologists like it for its brevity. Mort liked it because his score was perfect. He got 30 out of 30. It is rare for an elderly person who has AD to be able to score 24 or higher. One of his tasks was to write a sentence. The sentence has to have a subject and verb, and be sensible. The patient can still get credit despite faulty grammar and punctuation, but must produce it spontaneously rather than to dictation. Mort wrote, "The quick brown cow jumped over the mooning dog." I gave him credit for that.

I sent Mort my office note, which I dictated in the form of a letter to him with a copy to his doctor. My diagnosis at the time of our goodbyes in the office was, "Mort, you are one of the 'worried well.'" Time has proved me right: When I see him in the hall—we both return often to our place of previous employment—he has the same sagging shoulders and drooping mouth, but by mutual unspoken agreement, we let sleeping dogs lie. It had been embarrassing for him to have to tell a colleague that he thought he was becoming demented—whether he was or not.

That was really what was happening to "Sal," a neurologist in practice on the north side of the city at that same time. Sal was skilled and kindly, but he had to close his office at once on the day he was diagnosed as having early AD. His daughter kept me posted on his rapid decline. It was not long from the time he stopped seeing patients until he no longer knew his family. No amount of magical thinking can protect us from feeling vulnerable when those who succumb to disease (not just dementia, of course, but any serious medical condition) are cut from the same cloth as ourselves. I took it hard when my favorite teacher—among the many good teachers I knew during my residency in neurology at the Neurological Institute of Columbia-Presbyterian Medical Center in New York City—succumbed to AD. How, I asked, could that dapper man, so talented, so enthusiastic about his profession, so dedicated to excellence, slip away like that? I did not set out in this article to address that question or questions such as What causes AD? and How can I prevent it? (clearly, "Use it or lose it" is fatuous advice) but, rather, to look for ways of answering the question Mort asked me: "Am I really losing my mind?"

AAMI. It has also been called such things as *benign senescent forgetfulness*. For clinical and research purposes, it is a diagnosis applied to persons 50 years old or older. That isn't to say that healthy young people may not be forgetful in similar ways (although not to the same extent): We seniors face the daily difficulty of learning the names of people we meet, recalling phone numbers and zip codes, remembering where we put our keys and our glasses. I deliberately did not mention the car. The reason, I suspect, is that, in an article entitled "Is it Alzheimer's?" in a recent issue of Hospital Practice I read this: "A common initial symptom [of AD] is to return to the parking lot and not remember where the car is parked or to forget the way home." Not fair! Who doesn't have trouble finding the car? Now, if you left the grandchild in the back seat, that might be a different story. "Taken individually," the article continued, "most of the memory lapses that occur in early Alzheimer's disease are hard to distinguish from normal patterns of behavior. But eventually they aggregate, and at a certain threshold the spouse or someone else will seek medical attention for the patient." That, I concede, is true.

We who have AAMI have trouble shopping successfully without a list (a list that may have only three items on it; a list that is still on the kitchen table when we are frozen in front of a freezer in the supermarket). We do not do well at retrieving a piece of information right now, when it is still useful, instead of the next morning, when it has been passively presented to memory like a polished shell washed in on the high tide or, perhaps more aptly, like the bloated intestine of a mouse deposited on the doormat during the nocturnal predations of the family cat. It is often just a word that we (all right—that I) want. Because I have a large vocabulary, I can usually produce a synonym, and usually so adroitly that I hardly know I'm doing it; but if the word is one I rarely use, really want, and have relatively recently acquired, it may be a bear to bring to mind. Example: *ataxithymia*. It translates as "not touching the mind." It is not in my medical dictionary, but Ann and I read it somewhere (where?), and it means not being in touch with one's feelings. It is a word I wanted because it applies to the way I (neurologist/essayist; senior citizen/possible preclinical AD patient) was trying to approach this discussion, which could so easily touch a raw nerve. After scrabbling through my mental lexicon for days, I called a good friend who is a neuropsychologist, gave him the definition, asked if he knew the word (he didn't), and, before you know it, was making tentative arrangements to be tested formally for dementia! I think that word search had pushed me further than I wanted to admit. The more I wanted to remember it, the less successful I was. I was nixing memory with desire. Then, at 2:30 a.m., in the bathroom, I found it—"illuminated," Ann said next morning, "by the night light." It had taken four days. What's more, I had only begun to savor the honey of having shoved that bear of a word through a tight place in my memory when I thought, naturally enough, of Winnie-the-Pooh and how he was stuck in a hole at a friend's house after eating too much "Hunny," and how he had to stay stuck until he lost weight—and now I can't remember if he was at

Piglet's or somewhere else, and I realize that it is not just recent memory that is vulnerable. Kurt Vonnegut summed it up: "And so it goes."

I am not alone in complaining about my memory. I don't mean that my family is complaining. They are really too nice about it, and my wife is forever creating specious excuses for my lapses, in order to assuage my concerns. I mean that most older people have the same complaint. Among the numerous epidemiologic studies from which the Mayo Clinic derives a part of its fame is a group of investigations that goes by the lugubrious and presumably crafty acronym MOANS (Mayo Older Americans Normative Studies). One such study was an assessment of subjective memory complaints that provided these findings: Only one in eight older persons living in the community reports having no memory problems. Fewer than 3 percent of such people, however, consider their problems "major," and only a small proportion believe that their memory has changed substantially for the worse in the past five years.

On the objective side, these reports proved to be of little value. Although those persons who thought poorly of their memory were sometimes right, they were sometimes wrong, and the overlap was too great to make their opinion a substitute for testing. Of the 281 participants who provided the "longitudinal sample" in the five-year study, who were 55 years of age or older and "normal" to start with, only 11 were diagnosed as being cognitively impaired when the study ended. What did correlate best with subjectively poor memory? Psychological distress. As the Mayo investigators put it, "level of psychological distress was far more predictive of subjective memory complaint than absolute level of learning performance" on the memory tests. They caution against concluding that being depressed makes a person feel that he is losing his memory. It could be that people who hold a generally low opinion of themselves and their ability to control their lives would rate both memory and mood as being impaired, without providing support for a cause-and-effect relationship.

To illustrate the everyday problems we all face in recognizing dementia and deciding what to do about it, not only as potential patients but as friends and relatives, I will tell you briefly about two octogenarian women who came to have a meal with us just this past week. Both are Ann's long-time friends. Each lives alone. They were invited separately, on different days. Each of them has been to our house several times. Each one arrived to say that she had driven past the house, realized she had gone too far, and then turned around and found us.

"Lola," who is nearly 87, is an insomniac, subject to bouts of depression, but usually interested in her hobbies: genealogy and astrology. She comes from a long line of people who lived long lives and kept their wits about them. She herself has outlived two husbands. Although she lives alone, a son lives nearby and she keeps in close touch with all of her children, who help her to rally when she is feeling low.

Lola is confident of her own continuing capacities, and we agree. She is sharp, and good company. Just after I typed this paragraph, she called to ask me a question: What five U.S. presidents are not buried on U.S. soil? When I said I didn't know, she told me Ford, Carter, Reagan, Bush and Clinton. She got the question from a book on "brain building."

"Lily" is also in her 80s, but nobody has more exact information than that. She never married, and the companion who lived with her died three years ago of breast cancer. Lily is a former librarian, a voracious reader and, until perhaps a year ago, she was always ready to discuss her reading. Now the mainstay of her conversation has become questioning, and she asks each of her questions over and over: Is Ricky doing well in school? Is he in high school now? Is this a new car? (No, you have ridden in it before. Here, I'll help you with the seat belt.) Have you redecorated this room? (No, we have done some remodeling, but this room looks the way it has for the past three years.) When we ask her about her own life, she is dismissive: "Boring." No details. At the time of this last encounter, she had a hard time hearing Ann, who has a small voice, and Ann asked her why she was not wearing her hearing aids. "I don't have any," she replied. I called her on that one, but she insisted she had never owned aids. Then she corrected herself. "They are at home," she said. We suspect she has mislaid them.

We are confident about Lola: Despite the loneliness and depression, we think she will make it through life cognitively intact. Lily, we fear, is doomed. She has no relatives. She lives in a big house with a difficult dog she would not part with. (The dog is also showing signs of senility and has become a hazard. It has bitten her, and it is one of the things she manages to trip over.) She smokes (another hazard). When she came down with the flu, some weeks ago, and we stopped by to check on her, we found her sitting at the kitchen table with a bottle of whiskey—drunk, surly and despondent. Her housekeeper, who does not live there and, like us, had just come by to see how she was managing, was trying to get her to bed. We did not stay, and I will not keep you with her, either. It is really too sad.

Because we are not all doomed to dementia in old age and because we do not expect perfect performance from others (with the exception of concert pianists and bank tellers), we should try to keep a lid on the anxiety generated by our quotidian glitches, but it's hard: Yesterday, while I was putting up a towel rack, I spent as long finding and refinding one of the screws as I did in any other phase of the procedure. That example, like the one with which I led off this essay (don't look: it was the "varmint-screen caper,") is mundane, but that is exactly the reason it is so galling. We need to both admit our limits and affirm our capabilities, like Tennyson's Ulysses: "Tho' much is taken, much abides; and tho'/ We are not now that strength which in old days / Moved earth and heaven, that which we are, we are." But, without thinking of ourselves as heroes, we also need to keep striving, as did Ulysses: It is the tension between the wished-for and the feasible that produces the frustration of aging.

The way to confirm the presence of AAMI, if confirmation is required (because worry over the situation is beginning to depress and disable the individual, as it did Mort or because things are getting so bad that the family are worried, too) is to be interviewed and tested. This may require the collaboration of a neurologist and a neuropsychologist, ultimately but it should start with one's personal physician, because such things as depression and hypothyroidism, to cite single examples of emotional and physical disorders that can masquerade as dementia, need to be exposed by the approach of a generalist before the specialists get involved. The criteria for diagnosis of AAMI (as described by Dr. Thomas Crook, a memory-clinic director) include these: memory problems that have come on gradually, not suddenly;

scores below the cut-off on standardized memory tests, such as the Benton Visual Retention Test or the Logical Memory and Associate Learning subtests of the Wechsler Memory Scale; adequately functioning intelligence as determined by, for example, the Vocabulary subtest of the Wechsler Adult Intelligence Scale; and absence of dementia as indicated by the score achieved on the MMSE. I don't believe that Dr. Crook would maintain that vocabulary is not vulnerable to the aging process: There is difficulty in assimilating new words. (In my case, words such as *hermeneutics* and *epistemology*, which I have only recently decided I wanted to learn, have driven me back to the dictionary too many times to make my decision worth the bother.) Besides that, there are the words we think we have filed somewhere that won't come back. I started this essay by describing as "pieces of hardware" the gizmos I now know to call *turnbuttons*. I had to ask a friend who owns a hardware store. I knew they were not wingnuts or turnbuckles. But why would I look up the similar word *turnbuckle*, just to be sure it was not the right word, if the right word (which isn't in my unabridged dictionary) had not been lurking in the shadows of my memory? And didn't I already discuss vocabulary?

If a physician is consulted, the investigation must be thorough. Physical ailments such as low thyroid function, kidney failure and liver disease must be sought. Problems attributable to substance abuse — nice old ladies like Lily may be secret alcoholics, and she is—and to the drugs prescribed to treat physical and emotional disorders (especially tranquilizers, sedatives, antidepressants and other psychotropic agents) must be looked for. Alcohol is more likely to compound the memory problems than to cause them but, occasionally, the Wernicke-Korsakoff syndrome, brought on by severe nutritional deficiency and usually secondary to alcoholism, can wipe out recent memory. Special attention must be paid to the special senses, audition and vision. It is not possible to remove AD plaques from the brain, but it may help a lot to remove wax from the ears. Someone who does not hear well is likely to seem much less "with it" than he really is.

After all the other investigations have been completed, the neurologist may come to the conclusion that there is a familial or sporadic brain disease in progress—a *primary dementia*. Among those disorders, the most common and, today, the best known to the public is Alzheimer's.

In the dry language of a scientific journal, "a grossly impaired ability to acquire and retain temporally and spatially bound information is a hallmark of AD that occurs early in the pathogenesis." That kind of remembering is called *episodic memory.* It is what gives me the ability to recall that it was on the boulder near the big oak at the southeast boundary of her property that I first photographed Ann, who is now my wife. She was wearing the blue jacket she has finally given up wearing, jeans, and that Indian-design shirt she will never give up, on the first warm day of the spring of 1996. Again in psychologese, "in many instances, the degree to which an individual is able to utilize cognitive support in episodic memory tasks is related to successful use of semantic memory aids." Semantic—general—knowledge, such as how to speak English or perform an arithmetical operation or categorize, can in various ways come to the assistance of learners, young or old, who are not demented: If we can call on what we already know, we may be better able to commit new information to memory. We can follow instructions on how to organize the material, and we can also perceive a pattern for ourselves. We can take more time to learn, "enrich" the task by creating mental images (one of the well-known mnemonic "tricks"), and profit from hints ("cues") when we learn and when we try to retrieve what we have learned.

A person who has full-blown AD can do none of that well. "AD is associated with a reduced ability to use cognitive support for improving memory: a reduction in cognitive reserve capacity." It takes maximum effort to make AD patients do better (not well, but better): Support strategies have to be used both when they try to learn something (encoding) and when they try to bring it to mind (retrieval). Even then, AD patients "typically require more support than their healthy older counterparts to exhibit memory improvement." An explanation for "the reduced effects of cognitive support on memory in AD may be that the semantic network that guides the encoding and retrieval of episodic information functions less efficiently in AD." If you have heard the incoherent babbling of an AD patient in a far-advanced state of mental dilapidation you will find that to be a believable hunch about what is in progress. Our focus, though, is not on full-blown AD. It is incipient AD that is the concern. OK, my focus, my concern.

We have only to remember the jokes about Ronald Reagan when he was in office to recognize the shift in attitude we undergo when someone moves along the continuum. Only in retrospect can we be suspicious that what seemed laughable at the time was really ominous and not just the innocent absentmindedness we might have overlooked in somebody who did not have such an important job. But is AD only quantitatively different from AAMI? Is it correct to think of a slippery slope along which all of us with the wrong footwear will slide into mental oblivion? Observations to date are too limited to be reassuring.

The investigators at Stockholm's Karolinska Institute whose words appear above looked at a group of physically healthy elderly people (aged 75 or older). Some of them remained cognitively intact throughout the three years of the study (the normals). Some of them, although not demented by clinical criteria when initially tested, had become Alzheimer victims when they were retested three years later. The investigators called this subgroup "incident" AD patients, using the word *incident* in an epidemiological sense, to suggest that they "came down with the disease," if you will, during the time that the study was going forward. (It turned out that, collectively, the incident AD patients had not done quite as well as the normals when they took the MMSE the first time, but their scores had been above the formal cutoff for dementia.) The two subgroups also differed at baseline with specific regard to their episodic memory function, the incident AD patients again not doing as well as the normals. Both subgroups could make use of cognitive support—organizing, working slowly, using cues—but this support was not enough to make up for the deficits of the incident AD patients as compared with the normals. The graph showed parallel lines: The two groups, the normals and the incident AD patients, both improved with support, and to the same extent. This meant that there was still the same gap between them. If cued retrieval had proved capable of bringing the performance level of the incident AD patients up to normal, it would have suggested that retrieval was the predominant problem. But that did not happen. The problem had to be more than retrieval. The Swedish research workers and others think it is a problem with encoding—of moving information from primary (immediate or short-term) memory, which suffers little in mild to moderate AD, to secondary (long-term) storage. This is consistent with the finding on neuroimaging studies that the hippocampus and related parts of the temporal lobes atrophy early in AD. Those parts of the brain, neuroscientists believe, function in encoding, rather than in retrieval.

There was, in the Swedish study, a third subgroup, comprising 106 patients, whom they called "prevalent" AD patients because, although free from other diseases, they already had AD when they entered the study. Of course, they still had it three years later when they were retested, if they could be restested; 46 of them had died! Whether that was bad or good is not for me to say. I know what I would want for myself.

One group of people who have subjected themselves to scrutiny for the possible emergence of AD are healthy members of certain families in which genetically determined AD has appeared both early and often, as compared with the general population. The unnerving finding is that even in those persons who later develop aggressive (rapidly progressive) illness, there is a lengthy period during which, although there are no symptoms of dementia, there are selective deficits in verbal memory and in performance IQ. This can be looked upon as hopeful in the long run: A good protection for vulnerable neurons or a good treatment of early disease, when it becomes available, should obviously be started as soon as possible, and a leisurely onset of disease may permit treatment to be started when the signs are subtle and thus make it more effective.

Clinicians admit that they cannot confidently distinguish someone who shows "normal" age-associated cognitive change from someone on the cusp of AD, although I have detailed some of the ways that they are trying to do so. Neuropathologists, too, are unable to identify any feature of "age-related" neurodegeneration (the presumed neuroanatomical substrate of at least some AAMI) that absolutely sets it apart from the microscopic plaques and tangles that are the hallmark of AD. Plaques and tangles are numerous in AD, but they are present to some extent in aging normal brains as well. Because of those limitations, and because neuropathologists enter the picture after the subject's death, there is increasing interest in special laboratory tests that may help to predict the rate of an individual's progression into the seventh age of man. Authorities agree, though, that it is not a good idea for someone who does not have a strong family history of AD and who has no evidence of early dementia to be genetically tested or undergo MR scanning, since the findings will be hard to interpret and, at present, the therapeutic benefit of any treatment strategy is debatable at best. (Only one in 20 persons who go on to develop AD has an identifiable single gene mutation that reliably predicts the disease.) And even if there have been numerous cases in the family, it is the individual's right to choose not to know. We can all plan for the worst and hope for the best.

As I conclude this account, I think I have decided what to do about checking out my own memory bank. I want to undergo formal testing. My neuropsychologist friend is prepared to help. Maybe I have moved much of my savings to an account for which I have forgotten the number. Or maybe I have withdrawn and squandered a substantial amount and mislaid the withdrawal slips. Is there gold dust or just dust in my cranial vault? I'm not sure, but Ann can let you know, if you're interested. Give it some time, then get in touch with her. Probably it's best if you don't try to get in touch with me.

David Goldblatt, M.D., is Professor Emeritus of neurology and the medical humanities at the University of Rochester School of Medicine and Dentistry. He lives outside of Penn Yan, N.Y., on 17 acres of land, mostly former vineyards, much of which he keeps mowed in order to be able to find his way home more easily.

God, Glass, LSD:

A Memory

Greg Bottoms

My brother saw the face of God. You never
recover from a trauma like that. He was 14, on LSD, shouting for help
in the darkness of his room in our new suburban home. I was 10. I
stood watching from his doorway, still, eyes cinched up tight as seams,
trying to make out his writhing shape. I saw for myself. I didn't see
God, of course, but I saw my brother seeing God; I saw how petrified
he was, how convinced. I knew, still know, that he saw, in some form,
His or Her or Its face. It was in the window, a part of the night, shim-
mering over our neighborhood of new construction sites—clear plastic stapled to boards and waving in the night breeze, tire-tracked
mud, portable toilets.

God in the lives of men is nothing new. It's a story that unfurls
backward through the history of thought, meaning, reason. I've spent
a lot of time tracing it, reading it over and over, in a hundred different
ways. Characters change. There's a new setting, a twist in this plot that
wasn't in that one. But it is an old, old story, as old as Story itself. I
compare my brother with other narratives involving God. He, She, It
is the common language between us. That's how I place Michael,
make sense of him, re-imagine him—alongside saints and martyrs,
lunatics and heretics, those who have fallen, shaken and supplicant,
pleading, palms aimed heavenward, at the thought of God, His voice,
the sweet, terrible whisper in their ear.

Jesus. Abraham, Jacob, Paul. St. Mark, Luke, Matthew, John. Joan
of Arc, Hildegaard, John Brown. Charles Manson, Jim Jones, David
Koresh.

Blake saw angels in trees. Thoreau imagined the possibility of
divinity, the sublime, in a knothole. Whitman saw God in the salivat-

ing mouth of a soldier's bullet hole. Mother Teresa knew the force of God lived even in the fecal rivers of Asian cities, the venereal fever of a beaten whore. I used to watch a man who lived on the streets of Richmond, Va., who spent hours shouting "Jesus" while in paroxysms, drooling, his fly open. But they didn't see Him. None of them. Not like my brother.

So I dwell; I obsess; I remember in unmoored chunks, half-scenes, things that have to be pieced together, arranged.

That night, when I was 10, I couldn't move. The feeling of immobility, of being trapped, sticks in my mind. I stood in his doorway, a night-light golden behind me, wearing pajamas, fat-faced and freckled, looking at my brother while he screamed, all open mouth and high-pitched wail. His face was contorted like a snake handler's, like a strychnine drinker's in the documentaries I would watch years later, late at night, with a VCR remote in my hand.

I stood, squinting into darkness. The memory is a series of fragments. Maybe, at 10, with my eyes barely open, I saw the future. Maybe I saw in the dark of the room, heard in the screams, that one day soon he would be living on the streets, hungry; that he would be diagnosed as an acute paranoid schizophrenic; that he would leap from a van going 45 miles per hour to avoid institutionalization; that he would frighten women, children, neighbors, us; that he would be raped; that he would admit to a murder he didn't commit; that his face would be on the front page of local newspapers, the killer, the rapist; that he would attempt suicide for the first time by drinking Drano, the second time by hanging himself; that he would dismantle the fire alarms in my parents' home and light it on fire, ultimately ending up in a Virginia maximum-security prison, praying and crying, by then all but dead to me, locked away in a place I would never visit, a brother—the same curve of flesh, angle of jaw, color of eyes—who had become a few cryptic letters full of biblical quotes, who I don't think would recognize me.

I go over and over this. My memory is a scratched record: There I am, watching, cautious, afraid of him, afraid to step into the room, because of his early propensity for petty cruelties: charley horses and wedgies, dirt clods and airplane spins, skinned knees and bloody lips and mean laughter. The stuff of early childhood, of brothers, but from him: different, darker, done with an eerie pleasure.

He ripped a poster from his wall, knocked over a red lava lamp, the only source of light within the room, spreading glass, a viscous gel.

My father built this house in the suburbs, most of it by himself. He could still barely afford it, had to sign half his life away to a bank. But we were away from blacks and crime and bad neighbors and people as poor as we were. We were pretending, for the sake of appearances, that we had money, though the old rusty Ford Rambler in our driveway must have given us away. Our pretending was in the scent of new wood, the chemical stench of fresh, shaggy carpets; it was in the long blades of light through our new windows from the streetlight outside, in the feeling in my memory of cotton pajamas with feet in them, in my brother's screams. Our pretending was in the black-light posters, the ones that glowed sharply in my brother's room—Bruce Lee, Hendrix, Foghat, Lynyrd Skynyrd, Led Zeppelin, comic-book covers from "Conan the Barbarian" and "Heavy Metal" and the animated film "American Pop." Our pretending was everything we did and had. Our pretending is how we survived, how we hovered just slightly above our actual lives, which, over the years with Michael, felt increasingly unreal.

It seemed plausible to me then that God could be in our window. I sometimes felt a cool tingle, like the breath of an invisible congregant, during the hymns at church. Electricity surged through me during sermons—the stained glass, the pastor's booming voice, the organ notes in my stomach and testicles. It was wonderful and frightening, the best and worst feeling. I've spent my life, starting from this moment in my brother's room, at once doubting and believing, fearing and embracing God; or at the very least, the thought of God in me, in others. I'm an atheist and a true believer. I value reason and hope for transcendence. I value the four strange and very repetitive Gospels of Jesus as much as any books I've read, but I can't imagine attending a church now, listening to simple aphorisms and affirmations, having become acutely suspect of all proclamations.

But I believed God was there for Michael that night, hovering in the window. I don't mean a hallucination; I'm not speaking figuratively; I mean that what was in the window that night for Michael was as real as the skin on his face. He'd stepped outside of our tenuous collective reality and into alternate space, a space where God was a shape, a newly decipherable language.

He had been at an Ozzy Osbourne concert at the Coliseum. It was 1980. He'd dropped six hits of acid. In his room he was having his first psychotic break. It came in the form of crippling guilt, ruthless introspection. He was Jesus being scolded by an angry Father. He wore sin, all sin, heavy as lead shackles. God made him look at himself, and he was a stone with a miniscule heart.

He flailed. He cut his feet on the glass from the lava lamp. He turned and pleaded to and then punched a neon, glowing Bruce Lee. God was torturing him with the things he had inside himself, with his own feelings and memories. His thoughts were razor-sharp. He started breaking everything he touched. A piggybank in the shape of a football, spreading coins across the floor; his stereo case; a picture frame containing a family picture, each of us smiling under a blue sky against a blue, blue ocean.

But memory fades, tricks, becomes convenient, reshapes itself. It's been 19 years. I remember my mother and father there now, as if conjured from air or simple need, standing at the threshold of Michael's room. Glass scattered everywhere, shining like quartz.

My father hesitated. He wasn't much bigger than Michael, 5 foot 8 inches, 160 pounds. And Michael was swinging, the LSD pumping panic through his blood. My father knew. He wasn't surprised. He knew about the drugs and the heavy metal and the bad friends and the skipping school. Michael was a problem kid. Always had been. Foul-mouthed. Willing to experiment with anything. My father knew and wanted to change things, to make it better, but the kid was out of control, sometimes violent. He knew how simultaneously sophisticated and irresponsible kids were these days. They knew more than they could handle knowing. They'd granted themselves a dangerous, cynical sort of freedom. Sex at 12, 13. Drinking, drugs, even earlier. He knew. He even, if he had thought hard enough about it, knew that mental illness was our family's sickness. His mother had been institutionalized twice. His own father, who was dead, had lived in a terminal funk, carrying the weight of a world that he knew cared nothing for him. His grandfather in North Carolina had clenched the barrel of a 12-gauge between his teeth, spreading chunks of hair and bone and flesh along the wall, while his nine children were downstairs playing. Before this, my great grandfather, as Michael would soon had, had taken to quoting scripture at length, mixing dogma with threats and expletives.

If my father had thought about it while watching Michael that night, he'd have realized that the chances of his son seeing the face of God, in some form, were not so astronomical, even without the acid.

I looked up at him—he seemed like a giant—wondering what was required of me. He wore sweatpants and a night-league softball shirt with *Three Dog Night* stenciled across the chest. He had big sideburns and wavy auburn hair, was only six or seven years older than I am now, with the massive hands of a worker. He was barefoot. It was after midnight, and the stars out the window were more ground glass.

What do I remember about my mother? She was composed. She was withdrawn. She must have been crying. She's always been given to quick, private tears. Yes, she was foundering. She knew Michael better than anyone, is perhaps the only person who has ever really known him, even though he hid things from her, was secretive to the extreme. In fact, this was the last straw in an ongoing line of last straws that spread out in front of us like taillights on a highway. This was the last straw like taking him back in the house after kicking him out will be the last straw, the last straw like picking him up from jail will be, the last straw, really, until the next last straw, and then the next. She was motionless, out in the hall, cast in shadow from the low-wattage night-light.

These days she got calls from school, from neighbors, from the parents of girls her 14-year-old may have slept with. She got headaches she blamed on the stress of Michael. She prayed for Michael. She locked her bedroom door at night when my father wasn't home.

My father, I remember, clicked on the light. That simple move seemed dangerous, bold, courageous. The room felt charged, alive. Shards of broken glass the size of human teeth spread over the floor. The lava lamp's snot glistened on the new carpet. Michael calmed. The window had now become a mirror. Instead of the accusatory face of God, the angry father, he saw only himself, a pallid face and tears and eyes black as coal. His feet bled, were completely red with blood. I remember glass sticking out of them in different directions like sharks' teeth. My mother called for an ambulance. My father went to him, walking over the glass, not even considering the glass, and pulled him to his chest.

And I remember my father—who died one month before Michael went to prison in 1993—sitting on the bed, holding Michael, this big kid in an Ozzy Osbourne T-shirt sprawled awkwardly on his lap. They were rocking back and forth. Michael was slack, almost a corpse. He looked empty, drained of all life, of any former self.

I can see us all in my memory, even myself, the kid, the character, the narrator. It's quiet now. I smell the chemical newness of our home. I'm floating over my past, catching fragments of our lives, to make it into a story. I have an aerial view: I see myself seeing the first evidence of my brother's blossoming insanity; I hear my first fragmented thoughts of God, feel my first real spiritual dread; I see my mother rummaging through the bathroom medicine cabinet for Mercurochrome, Band-Aids; and I see my father—I see this most clearly—holding Michael, probably for the last time, holding him like an infant, shushing him, rubbing his hands through his sweaty hair. Their feet drip blood into a small puddle as if from one vein.

My father is whispering. I lean in, listen. He is telling us it will all be fine.

Greg Bottoms' *memoir, "Angelhead," from which this essay is excerpted, will be published next year by Crown.*

Thoughtprints

James Glanz

During electrical stimulation of electrode No. 24 … the patient stated that all faces in the room appeared indistinguishable.
—*Trevor Mundel, et al., "Experience-Based Configural Face Encoding in the Human Right Fusiform Gyrus," preprint, The University of Chicago*

My yellow cat has epilepsy. The first time I was to witness one of its seizures, a quasihuman scream, torn from some fabric of terror and despair, startled me awake at about 3 a.m. I found the cat convulsing behind the tall mirrored doors of a closet that stood partially open near the head of my bed. Gripped by sheer befuddlement, I bellowed and thrust the doors apart, shattering one of them, and saw the cat lying on its side, eerily gagging as if being throttled, while spasmodically, fiercely clawing against no visible threat beyond the shoes and slippers lined up in tidy rows in the closet. The spasms slowed, becoming more tortured, until it seemed certain that the cat was dying for lack of breath. Then the cat sat up on its front paws.

The convulsions had abruptly stopped. The scent of urine rose from the closet in the room's sudden stillness. With huge black pupils, the cat stared straight ahead, as if absorbed in some terrible secret, and I had the 3-a.m. impression that shards of its meager *self* were returning from the jagged slopes of planets that the sane of this universe have never seen. My presence had no more effect on that stare than the bed or the floor lamp did. When, minutes later, the cat finally recognized me, it began to purr.

Standing there, conscious of the smell of pee and the first stirrings of regret over the smashed door, I recalled, through one of the connections that may or may not say something worth knowing about how the mind works, that the Grateful Dead had been in town several years before, playing at Soldier Field, next to the lake, in one of Jerry Garcia's last concerts. A bike path meanders past Soldier Field and its parking lots, where a whole shantytown of Deadheads in tie-dyed shirts had camped peacefully. They shuffled along the bike path in formations that suggested a flotilla of rafts with many agendas and few astrolabes. The day before the concert, approaching the rear straggler of one such group on my mountain bike, I slowed and slowed, hoping the gentle soul would notice me looming and puffing behind him. Instead I came too close and rode up his ankle with the knobby treads of the bike's front tire. The action of the treads ripped a dirty Converse sneaker off the back of his foot, and when I braked, the tire pinned his shoe, and him, to the spot. He twisted awkwardly around to look at me. I do not remember his face. He said this: "Sorry, man."

I do not remember his face. Memory aside, my notes on scientific topics are obsessive and, above all, dated, so that once a new closet door had been ordered (Rubenstein Lumber Company, 167 North Morgan Street, Chicago, tel: 312-666-4800), I combed both my notes and old newspapers in the library across the street from my apartment for any clue to a psychic link between grand mal and Garcia. This turned up: "We have a paucity of animal models that accurately represent human epilepsy," a neurosurgeon had explained to me on that same afternoon, July 23, 1994, a Saturday.

The afternoon shone again when I read this line. I had rushed the end of the bike ride in order to be home for his call, which dealt with experiments involving slices of rat brain pierced by a pair of electrical probes in a dish. A potassium solution in the dish caused neurons in the brain slice to fire chaotically, as if it were beginning an epileptic seizure. Precisely timed jolts from one of the probes could make the seizing behavior stop. To achieve this end, the other probe monitored the brain's own moment-to-moment pattern of firing and sent this information to a computer, which in turn calculated the time sequence of the jolts to be applied by the first probe. The neurosurgeon said that this general technique, called *chaos control*, for stopping seizures could someday jump straight from the *in vitro* experiments to human trials, since live animals—his "models"—are often useless in the testing of potential epilepsy treatments.

Not before trudging backward in time from the smashed mirror was it impressed upon me how astonishing this mathematical control of brain tissue was, this conductor waving a baton before an orchestra of potassium-drunk rat neurons. Much later an epileptologist explained to me why studying the disease in live animals was often not very effective. Among other reasons, mental disturbances have an intensely subjective quality; they must be described by those who suffer and receive treatment. Human epileptic seizures, for example, may be preceded by the *aura*—an unaccountable sense that someone has entered the room, a feeling of nausea, an apparent odor, or some other recognizable sign. "You can't ask a cat if it's having a déjà vu experience," said the epileptologist.

This collision of subjectivity and the computable math of chaos generated a shower of sparks in my own mind. The metaphor itself, I knew, must be dancing like a St. Elmo's fire among the associative sulci of my cortex, a realization that would have its own chaotic center of combustion. I wanted to know whether such techniques should be seen as just another mechanical procedure—no more a personal invasion than an X-ray of someone's pelvis—or whether they would open the first, big-eyed gaze by science into an irreducibly human place, into once-hidden reflexes that could not be set apart from ourselves as easily as the bending of a joint or the contraction of a muscle or even the aimless flutter of an electroencephalogram. Could the dread of a 3-a.m. thought be skewered like an insect on a pin and displayed, in some virtual glass case of the future, with a crisp and technically accurate paragraph describing a prior belief that this well-studied specimen constituted the soul?

There was also an entirely benign perspective on all of this neural probing, of course. Call it the view from the 3-p.m. cortex. As the neurosurgeon and mathematician Steven Schiff explained it to me once in an email, a central problem in neuroscience today goes like this: "Think a moment about the 'binding problem' ... You are reading this text, decoding the images and thinking of the language it implies, formulating your response and scribbling notes on a pad. How are your perceptions 'bound together' at spatially disparate parts of your brain?" What's needed is some generalized way of looking at the noisy, imperfect synchrony or coupling between the electric or magnetic or metabolic activity in those disparate parts. Making connections, realizing patterns—humans do those things well, but how? The same mathematical unraveling that applies to the chaotic patterns of epilepsy could indeed tease apart the fine weave that links ordinary neurons in the brain.

Still other facts could override the subtle *soucis* of the healthy. It is quite possible that insights like these could offer some peace not just to the ill but also to the incurably tormented—those whom drugs do not help and who cannot even benefit from the therapy of last resort: the removal of diseased or damaged foci of their brain from which seizures seem to emanate, like a subterranean explosion. During my immersion in these subjects, I have learned of children afflicted with 30 seizures a day. I have met other people with less-frequent seizures whose lives the disease has nevertheless smashed by preventing them from attending school or holding a job or escaping misery at its most personal levels. The most baffling and idiosyncratic disability of all turned up in a woman whose aura temporarily took from her the ability to distinguish between different faces. By stimulating her epileptic focus with an electrode prior to surgery, a team of physicians, led by another clinician-mathematician, John G. Milton of the University of Chicago, found that they could induce the state at will. The crucial position lay under an electrode, designated No. 24, in an array resting upon her brain.

this morning i whispered your name this morning the clouds dropped low over atlanta this morning the clouds this morning anna i whispered the clouds they covered all that we have forgotten this morning atlanta i whispered this morning

From one point of view, there is nothing particularly inscrutable about a neuron. Mathematically, ensembles of neurons merely show that simple entities interacting in simple ways can exhibit behavior patterns of incredible complexity. There are roughly as many neurons in the human brain as stars in our galaxy. Yet the Milky Way, with its 10 to 100 billion glowing orbs and their affiliated nebulae, dust, planets and cosmic small change, is in most respects a simpler object than the brain. It has become a cliché among cosmologists that the physiology and behavior of a single frog is more complicated than the large-scale evolution of the entire universe. Much of that complication can be traced to the frog's crisscrossing network of neurons.

Focus on the essentials, however, and any one of those neurons, or nerve cells, is not such a messy thing. Each consists of a soma, or cell body, from which generally emerges a branching shrubbery of so-called dendrites and a single axon that ranges from less than a milli-meter to more than two meters in length. The terminus of the axon often branches as well. Under the right conditions, a train of voltage spikes called *action potentials* ripple down the axon from the soma at speeds as great as 100 meters a second and more.

When those nerve impulses reach the axon tips, a chemical called a *neurotransmitter* can be released into a microscopic gap, or synapse. On the other side of that synapse is a dendrite, soma or axon of another neuron. The spritz of neurotransmitter is a form of commu-nication from one neuron to another, in effect letting the second neuron know that the axon termini of the first are tingling with action potentials.

What induces a neuron to fire off a string of action potentials in the first place? It "integrates," or adds up, all the information arriving from all the synapses it has with the axon termini of other neurons. A synapse may be excitatory—that is, tending to cause a recipient neu-ron to fire—or inhibitory, suppressing the firing. Envision a stock trader listening on three different phones, staring at prices on a com-puter screen and generally taking in the chatter and commotion of the other traders around her. At any moment the totality of that information might push the trader to take an action, such as buying or selling; or the tips from the bulls and bears might cancel each other so that the trader does nothing. Any particular neuron can receive inputs from as many as 100,000 synapses, leading to biological cir-cuitry of unimaginable complexity—such as the trader.

Most of the knottiness follows from the connections themselves. But individual neurons do have tricks of their own, even when regarded as nothing more than circuit elements. In a noted experi-ment, John Rinzel of the Center for Neural Science at New York University, and the late Rita Guttman stimulated a squid giant axon with electrical current. At high values of the current, the axon fired repetitively, and at low values it was silent. At intermediate values, however, slight perturbations in the current could make it jump between the firing and quiet states, a phenomenon called *hysteresis* or *bistability*. Computer models have been made of bistable neurons linked into networks—perhaps a vast simplification of the brain. The models show the linked neurons behaving like dogs in the backyards of a big neighborhood: If one dog barks, all the rest may start up, but once they fall silent, most of them may sleep through the afternoon. "The network itself would be bistable," Rinzel told me three years and six weeks after the Dead concert.

If epilepsy turned out to be a manifestation of bistability in the human brain, physicians would have been granted a clue on how to treat it. But I am getting ahead of myself.

Networks of just a few neurons display surprising and sophisticated behaviors in nature. If the tail fin of a crayfish is carefully removed, electronics can monitor the firing of its mechanoreceptor system. The small network of sensory neurons in this system soak up information from the surroundings directly. The system has a stimulus threshold: Swish the fin hard enough through water and hairs on the fins move, inducing the sensory neurons to send trains of spiky voltage impulses down their axons. But suppose you rig a machine to swish the fin back and forth gently enough that the stimulus is barely *subthreshold*, or too weak to generate a signal on the neurons. Now add *noise* to the oscillation. By *noise* I mean a random, herky-jerky motion. You might imagine that the noise would make it even more difficult for the mechanoreceptor to perceive the weak oscillation. It was the achievement of the biophysicist Frank Moss to show that as the noise amplitude is gradually cranked up, the receptor neurons actually begin to encode the oscillation in their patterns of firing with greater and greater fidelity.

With increasing noise amplitude, that fidelity rises to a peak and then falls off as the oscillation is swamped completely. Perhaps it makes sense that this phenomenon, which has been named *stochastic resonance*, should have evolved to govern the perception of animals in the wild. Put yourself in the place of a crayfish or a cricket (whose perception of oscillatory wind currents, as generated by loudspeakers in a lab, has also been shown to exhibit stochastic resonance) that is about to be threatened by the swift and stealthy approach of a predator. Whether driven by the undulation of a fish's body or the beating of a bird's wings, oscillatory motions of the medium surrounding the prey *in the presence of natural, random, wind gusts or water currents* will serve as your warning of approaching death. Sensitivity amid the confusion of your environment will determine whether you, a lonely cricket, hop in time to escape that big, hungry, incoming beak.

You might take that tale as a mathematical parable: Stochastic resonance shows up in human neurons, too. If subjects rest a finger on a subtle, computer-controlled indentation that pulses up and down, the action may be imperceptible at first. But if either electrical or mechanical noise is added to the indentation and experimenters ask the subjects when they can feel the regular movements, the percentage of correct responses rises and then falls as the noise gets stronger. Other experiments have tested human proprioception, or the sense of where a limb is in space, when a sharpened tungsten wire is poked into the arm and vibrated against the radial nerve, about midway between the elbow and the shoulder. The noise created by nothing more than a 10-micrometer vibration could enhance a subject's ability to sense whether his or her wrist had been flexed by a small angle—a degree or two.

Such research is unlikely to help "the disembodied lady" who was memorably described by Oliver Sacks in "The Man Who Mistook His Wife for a Hat"—a woman who had lost all sense of proprioception and had to relearn simple actions like walking and sitting up. But the results could provide relief in smaller ways. There is a project at Harvard Medical School to use stochastic resonance for improving the rehabilitation prospects of stroke patients and of diabetics and elderly people with peripheral neuropathy, a deadening of sensation in the extremities. The idea is to develop gloves and socks outfitted with hundreds or thousands of piezoelectric noise inducers. They might help patients maintain good posture while walking and keep them aware of numb limbs, reducing injuries (from falls) and infections (from sores that go unnoticed). "The sensory loop is so essential," Casey Kerrigan, a rehab specialist at the medical school, told me once. "They use the feeling to relearn a motor task. This could really help."

The relationship between stochasticity and sense could go deeper. Still other experiments have suggested that during precision motor tasks, the human brain and peripheral nervous system might actually generate their own internal noise in order to sharpen proprioception, like dentists who do their best work next to a television turned up loud.

*houses across the mississippi those banks those bluffs a sunday a porch
houses when the mississippi rose murky above the flats you stood on those
bluffs those banks were mine the mississippi the flats a sunday houses
above the flats houses a sunday when the mississippi rose a train bridge
houses*

In this mingling of physics, biology, mathematics and the habitat
of the mind, there are hints that the attempt to understand neural
complexity is not hopeless. The Darwinian tangled bank of interwoven
neurons does seem to preserve some elements of simplicity. That
includes stochastic resonance itself, whose existence mathematicians
say depends only on the presence of noise and a weak signal in any
system with some sort of threshold. Consider, as a general illustration
of those elements, a coin resting in one of two indentations in the
dashboard of a car that is winding along a country road. By themselves,
centrifugal forces on the coin might not be enough to shove it
from one receptacle to another. But if the road is bumpy or uneven
enough, the lateral component of this "noise" could sometimes help
centrifugal force nudge the coin across in one direction or the other.
If the road is too rough, though, the coin can move whether the car is
turning or not, and the "signal" of the curves gets drowned out.

The signature of stochastic resonance reveals itself there in the
optimum noise level. The degree of force needed to push the coin
from one side to the other is the automotive analog of a neuron's
stimulus threshold. There exist formulas filled with sines, cosines,
epsilons and omegas to describe stochastic resonance in the most general
terms, but those results are just one spanner in a mathematical
toolbox that biology is beginning to open. Already far down the road
in my obsession with these matters, I put it this way in a news article
for Science in September of 1997:

Recordings of epileptic seizures, along with other studies of
activity in human and animal brains, are linking neuroscience
with a rarefied branch of mathematics called nonlinear dynamics.
This discipline was born as theorists tried to make sense of the
complicated rhythms of everything from wildly swinging pendulums
connected by springs, to the patterns formed by chemical

reactions on a metal surface, to wave trains steepening and crash-ing on a beach. Now a coterie of neuroscientists, biophysicists and mathematicians is finding that the same concepts can also help them understand the collective dynamics of billions of inter-connected neurons in the brain.

The article went on to explain that, like water molecules in a Waikiki breaker, neurons and their interactions are certainly laden with reductionistic details—cation channels, myelin sheaths, postsyn-aptic potentials—that get fuzzed out in this picture. Nonlinear dynamics finds regular patterns by examining these systems in the large. This approach is nothing new, since you don't learn to surf by studying the bipolar chemistry of liquid H_2O, but by appreciating the collective dynamics of waves containing 10^{29} molecules and more.

To continue with this brief exploration of psychohydrology, sup-pose you are lying awake at night, and for reasons you yourself do not fully understand, you are carefully timing the drips from a leaky fau-cet as they fall into a stainless-steel sink in the kitchen. Dripdrip drip … drip, drip, dripdripdrip dripdrip. Et cetera. Call the time interval between drip number n and the previous one X_{n-1} and the interval between n and the following one X_n. Each time there is a drip, imag-ine a point flashing on a two-dimensional screen in which the dis-tance along one axis of a graph is X_{n-1} and the distance along the other is X_n. The point will wander as if it were a ball rolling through a terrain of slopes, peaks, valleys and saddle-shaped regions. The pre-cise topography of that terrain might depend on the details of all the plumbing between your nocturnal faucet and the metropolitan water-works, not to mention the size of the leak, the fluid microturbulence inside the drops and the chemical hardness of the water. But for a par-ticular set of conditions, the terrain is fixed, and in your insomniac moments you have managed to grasp the essential structure of a sys-tem that would otherwise be complicated beyond human ken.

The charm of the method is that you can apply it to any dynam-ical system with a fascinating rhythm. A sputtering laser, a surging electrical circuit, an orbiting planet, a fibrillating heart, the annual population of spiders in a meadow, the firing of globs of neurons *in vitro* or *in vivo*—they all reveal something of themselves in one of these plots, which are known as *Poincaré* sections. In this vision, the neural ensembles would be firing and monitored en masse, in some collective fashion, rather than as individuals. As soon as a complicated system like the neurons has been abstracted in this fashion, all sorts of games can be played with the point as it rolls about. In 1990 three physicists—Edward Ott, Celso Grebogi and James Yorke—developed the mathematics of a kind of generalized pacemaker, which they called chaos control, for pinning the system at specific places in the Poincaré landscape.

An ordinary, unimaginative pacemaker applies regular jolts to a system, such as an erratically beating heart, in order to force it back into what is called a period-one *orbit* (the term is used by analogy with whirling planets) in which $X_n = X_{n-1}$. That steady pattern corresponds to a regularly dripping faucet: drip drip drip drip. But the faucet, like any of the other systems, could display periodicity of a different kind: dripdrip dripdrip dripdrip *or* dripdripdrip dripdripdrip *or* drip dripdrip drip dripdrip drip dripdrip. The dripdrip sequence displays period-two behavior, since it takes two drips to repeat, and for similar reasons dripdripdrip *and* drip dripdrip are period-three sequences. More generally, the faucet can slip into and out of these and any number of more complicated unstable periodic orbits, or UPOs. The techniques of chaos control can trap the system near any one of these UPOs, not just at the period-one specialty of a pacemaker.

Certain chaotic raconteurs like to compare this feat to a walrus balancing a beach ball on its nose. It might be more like balancing a marble on a saddle: The Poincaré landscape around UPOs is saddle-shaped, so the point representing the system tends to fall away from them in what would be the direction of the stirrups, but does no more than roll back and forth in the perpendicular direction. Control consists of either nudging the saddle over as the system point is about to fall off, or nudging the point itself back up to the crown of the saddle. The nudges would be applied only now and then—whenever the system began falling away from the UPO, like the walrus occasionally twitching its nose to keep the beach ball from falling off—and not by imposing a pacemaker's sledge-like regularity.

Practically speaking, controllers do the nudging by different means in the different systems. Moving the saddle corresponds to tweaking something physical about the system, like the resistances or inductances of a circuit or the defective washer in the faucet. Because manipulating the hardware is all but impossible in biological systems, experimenters turn to the second method for them, giving the system point a judicious push at just the right moment to put it back in the saddle. Just what this means was first demonstrated in 1992 with slices of rabbit heart in a dish. A nice hunk of ventricle beat regularly every 0.8 second if left to itself, a drip-drip pattern that might be represented symbolically as AAAAAAA … . Of course, experimenters did not leave the ventricle to itself, instead poisoning it with the drug ouabain, which speeded up the beating and induced arrhythmias. As the ouabain took effect, the heart began beating in a period-two pattern, with a long interval followed by a short interval (ABABAB …). Then the heart skipped in and out of period-four patterns (ABCD-ABCD …) and eventually started rambling all over the Poincaré map.

For cardiology buffs, the period-two pattern is called *bigeminy* and the period-four, *quadrigeminy.* (This might also be a good place to note that a senior researcher on the experiment was the aptly named Bill Ditto of the Georgia Institute of Technology.) Experimenters wanted to trap the rabbit heart at chosen UPOs, starting with period one, but not by hammering the preparation with electricity on every beat. They first watched the system point move around on the Poincaré map for a while. That told them the orientation and steepness of the saddles centered on the UPOs, just as looking at skiers from an airplane reveals a resort's topography, even if the mountains look flatter than paper. The Poincaré landscape went into a computer. It could then anticipate how fast and in what direction the system point would leave any UPO it approached. The controlling nudge was cleverly applied by firing an electrode to shorten a beat interval as the point slipped off the saddle. In other words, the undisturbed beat pattern, as anticipated by the computer, would have taken the point away from the UPO; the truncated pattern, effected by jolting the rabbit heart, set the point right on top of the saddle again, popping away with a fixed periodicity.

The Ditto device could trap rabbit hearts in the AAAAAAA, ABABAB, ABCABC or ABCDABCD patterns. "During chaos control, only every third or fourth beat was an electrically paced beat," the team reported in one of a series of publications on the experiment. After speculating about basing "smart pacemakers" on chaos control, some of the team members went straight from rabbit hearts to rat brains, joining forces with Steven Schiff, a former co-director of the epilepsy program at the Children's National Medical Center and now a professor of neurobiology and psychology at George Mason University. It was to discuss the latter experiments that I rushed home through Deadheads engaging in collective behavior along the lake. Like many chaos researchers, Schiff, a hypermath with a surgeon's ostentatiously deliberate diction, first became interested in the subject by reading James Gleick's "Chaos: Making a New Science" (Viking, 1987; this factoid sticks in my mind for a reason. Because of the similarity of our names, a few overlapping interests and the justified fame of Gleick's work, I sometimes arrive at scientific conferences to find myself assigned a press cubbyhole bearing his name. Thus I have a message for the world: I am not James Gleick.)

The terse response from Schiff's secretary to one of my earlier phone calls—"He's in OR. Can I take a message?"—effectively informed me that I was not dealing with a laboratory dreamer. His long-term aim was to find new ways of treating focal epilepsy in its most refractory forms. Drugs are ineffective against those forms of the disease, and surgical removal of the focus carries the risk that patients will lose some degree of motor function, memory or language skills. Sometimes the focus sits so far within or behind *eloquent* cortex—the term of art for regions whose loss results in obvious deficits—so that surgery is unthinkable. Schiff explained epileptic foci as confused lumps of neurons that either never formed properly or were somehow scarred from an injury and reconfigured into a cranial Balkan region, ready at any time to erupt with dystopia and send shock waves ricocheting through the rest of the brain. *Rewired* was the word he used, with reference to neural connectivity.

The experiment itself was modest compared to those great goals, as Schiff continually stressed. It was performed on slices of rat hippocampus in a dish. Part of the limbic system, which in humans governs emotions such as fear or rage or joy and is often swept by waves of stimulation during a seizure, the hippocampus itself is critical for memory. A stiff potassium solution got the hippocampus jumpin' and jivin'. More literally, its neurons began firing at irregular intervals in a way reminiscent of the so-called *interictal spikes* recorded before and after seizures in humans with epilepsy. As a first approximation at least, normal neural behavior is more like the unsynchronized noise of a crowd of people. The spikes appear when ensembles of neurons fire together, like an intoxicated orchestra being led by a mad conductor who changes the time signature, the key and the composer every few beats.

The Poincaré map for this hepped-up rat brain again revealed the system lingering around periodic points, then falling off the saddle. There were actually some advantages to working with brain instead of cardiac tissue. The brain was not in the process of dying, as the ouabain-poisoned heart was, and the times between successive interictal spikes could either be shortened—as in the earlier experiment—or lengthened. The difference was the neurons' susceptibility to both inhibition and stimulation. A double pulse from the electrode, it turned out, forestalled an anticipated spike, while a single pulse quickened its arrival. The tempo became *spiritoso* but sane. "We achieved better control than in the heart," an awed Bill Ditto told me by phone just after the Dead had left town. "This system in principle could have been much more irregular. It's thinking. Or trying to. It's really kind of scary. In the heart I never worried about, 'I wonder if this thing's adapting to what we're doing.'"

Because it is still unclear whether increasing or decreasing the periodicity might better avert seizures in the human brain, Ditto and Schiff also performed an exercise they dubbed *anti-control*, slapping the system away from periodicity whenever it got close. Where would the work go from there? As Schiff and I kicked that question around, it transpired that he had never read Michael Crichton's "The Terminal Man," the tale of Harry Benson, a man who has computer-controlled electrodes implanted in his brain to suppress a violent form of epilepsy. Of course the scheme eventually gets out of control and Harry Benson goes berserk. He is shot to death as he attacks one of the surgeons in a computer room. "Dr. Ross," Benson says, advancing on her as she points a gun with a trembling hand, "you're my doctor. You wouldn't do anything to hurt me." Far from showing the least discomfiture (I should have known better), Schiff complimented Crichton's overall prescience and still makes a habit of citing the book in his review papers.

milan berlin prague toulouse venice milan the frankfurt steel station the american lady has no dollars to bribe milan berlin prague berlin prague the post communist conductor your face your voice the clochard in paris toulouse venice milan no dollars no francs i speak no french do you think i am stupid you are reading le figaro american lady has no dollars wagonlit schlafwagen your face your voice toulouse venice milan le figaro stupid clochard gazetta dello sport it's raining marseilles the american frankfurt your face your voice wagonlit schlafwagen keine couchette bitte milan venice toulouse prague berlin milan venice milan

"We're watching 'The Nutty Professor!'"

George's mother, wearing a bright floral blouse, tries to remain cheerful. Her son is sitting cross-legged on a hospital bed, facing the television, a mass of multicolored wires emerging from a dome of white bandages on his head and running to a tower of electronics and computer screens near the door of the small room. She and his physician, John G. Milton, director of the University of Chicago Epilepsy Center, are waiting for George to have a seizure so that traces from the scalp electrodes can be analyzed prior to surgery. This edgy watch is a standard phase of pre-op for the eventual removal of an epileptic focus. Despite treatment with phenobarbital and other drugs, George had 10 seizures in the past month, by his mother's calendar, a rate ensuring that his behavior and the circumstances of his life still revolve around the disease. "They won't let him back into a normal school, because they don't have the people to take care of him," she says.

George snickers at that. Otherwise he does not have much to say. He is 12 or so, wearing shorts and a blue T-shirt with the word *adidas* printed over his heart. When a seizure is imminent, his face assumes a saturnine stare, his lips flare out and his left arm curls up tightly. He falls, then tries to get up and run. The seizures last from two to seven minutes. But in the high-tech hospital room that would be costing $10,000 a day if the family were paying full price, George has not managed a seizure yet.

Milton, a very short, fit and gregarious mathematician (his Ph.D. is from McGill University in Montreal) turned clinician, jokes about the tense scene. "I told him, 'If you get two good ones, you'll be ready to go,' " he says, glancing for a reaction from George. Nothing. George's attention is on "The Nutty Professor." As I am leaving the room with Milton, he tries once more, reaching up to grab an angle of the steel box that partly shrouds the tower of electronics. "We've had them hanging off this corner!" Milton exclaims, grinning and lolling his head in caricature of a seizure. Nothing. He hurries down a corridor, still smiling, his lab coat flapping behind him as he rattles off details of George's condition. The casual demeanor is probably more than a pose for Milton, who recently married into a family of professional golfers. In one of my first opportunities to speak with him, he reached me on a cell phone from the basement of his home, responding to my written request for a major interview on the non-linear dynamics of the brain. Milton wanted to know if we could take care of the interview while he finished cleaning his clubs.

At the hospital, he describes the much more telling series of tests that await George if he is approved for surgery. His skull will be opened so that an array of small, disk-shaped electrodes can be placed under his dura mater, the tough covering of the brain. Those electrodes in their flexible packaging look like shrink-wrapped lozenges of some indeterminate flavor. Once George's skull has been closed again, the electrodes will be used in two ways. First, they will receive signals passively during seizures, operating as a kind of radar to pinpoint the location of the epileptic focus. Second, the electrodes will be actively stimulated to map functional areas that must be avoided during surgery. When a particular electrode is stimulated, a patient's arm might twitch, or he might suddenly remember a long-forgotten scene or a piece of music. "I feel orange," a patient told Milton once. He never figured that one out.

It is precisely during these routine procedures that Milton and Schiff and their colleagues could carry out the first, tentative tests of theories of nonlinear brain dynamics on consenting patients. Because repeated stimulation of the electrodes during functionality mapping has no lasting impact on patients, the chance of any side-effects in such tests is remote, "The Terminal Man" notwithstanding. The stimulation would simply be done in accordance with a chosen theory instead of randomly. There could be simultaneous monitoring of brain activity, with feedback, just as in the case of the rat hippocampus. Clinicians, of course, are rightly cautious, and while proposals have been made and protocols discussed—and early explorations begun—little is being reported publicly at this point.

The exact strategies and algorithms to be used will clearly depend on which dynamical theory a researcher favors for the epileptic brain. Milton, who claims that Canadian genealogical researchers have established his family's probable descent from the man who wrote the words *At which the universal host up sent/A shout that tore hell's concave, and beyond/Frighted the reign of Chaos and old Night* (mm-hm, the poet; a fact producing the inevitable scrub-room witticism that goes, "Have you read the John Milton trilogy? 'Paradise Lost,' 'Paradise Regained,' and 'Dynamics of Small Neural Populations' "), is not himself a booster of chaos and UPOs and all that. Milton is more of a bistability man. He says that physicians going all the way back to Hippocrates and Galen noticed that loud noises or other stimuli could cause someone to snap out of a seizure. One of his favorite stories involves a girl whose seizure broke off prematurely when her startled mother dropped a trash can, and there actually is an FDA-approved device on the market that does no more than electrically stimulate the vagus nerve, in the neck, every few minutes, bringing partial relief to some epilepsy sufferers who do not respond to other treatment.

No one really knows why the vagal nerve stimulator works, when it does. Milton sees bistability in the mist. Whatever the underlying and obscure complexities, the brain is being batted from state A to state B, Milton thinks. He is inclined to aim for a more sophisticated version of the vagal nerve stimulator that would sense the onset of a seizure and apply jolts directly to the region around the focus in the brain. There is not necessarily a disconnect between the Miltonian and Schiffian world views, since the diagnostics and the jolt philosophy and even the states A and B could turn out to be based on UPOs and chaos, although no one knows that yet, either. Chaos or no chaos, the central mystery is still the shockingly short journey between disease and health, convulsions and calm, paradise lost and regained. "Why should this happen at all?" asks Milton.

Lately he has had even more reason to raise his palms skyward, as though caught in some intellectual bunker in front of the 14th green, and pose that question to the gods. His encounter with prosopagnosia has brought home both the potential power and the almost whimsical specificity of direct monitoring and stimulation. The experience might also teach us something about our extraordinary ability to recognize and discriminate human faces. I caution that I have not yet had a chance to meet this patient, and am relying for my information mainly on a brief, published abstract describing the research and a longer preprint that has been submitted to a technical journal and kindly provided to me in advance by the authors.

The basics of the story are quickly told. A 23-year-old, right-handed nurse with a decade-long history of medically refractory seizures was unable to distinguish the faces of people in her presence at the time of her aura. Lesions of the posterior right hemisphere, where the patient's epileptic focus was located, are known to cause the condition, prosopagnosia, on a permanent basis, and the study of such cases has greatly augmented what is understood about the processing of faces by the human brain. But because the syndrome often comes about in the context of a stroke, physical trauma or a brain tumor, disentangling prosopagnosia from other, more generalized deficits can be difficult. The patient agreed to allow a study by Milton and several colleagues of her *transient* condition with imaging and electrodiagnostic equipment (the first time this had been done) during routine tests with a subdural electrode array as she was being prepared for epilepsy surgery.

First, Milton presented her repeatedly with faces and monitored the *evoked potentials*, or electrical response, on the electrodes. The response was maximal at electrode No. 24, located in a specific cortical region called the *right fusiform gyrus*, which had been identified as important for human face processing in previous studies. The seizure focus itself was about 2.5 centimeters anterior to this electrode. Milton also checked the response to other types of visual stimuli: The evoked potential for strings of numbers and letters was maximal at an electrode a centimeter away from No. 24, and the small array picked up no response at all to checkerboard patterns of various colors and check sizes. Natural scenes did produce maximal responses at No. 24;

but compared to those for faces, they were delayed and of lower amplitude.

The next step was to stimulate No. 24 electrically. At *baseline*—that is, when the patient was in a normal state and the electrode was not being stimulated—she had no obvious problem with face processing. That changed when a 10-second train of square-wave pulses carrying 0.002 amps of current was applied to electrode No. 24. At that point, according to the report, "the patient stated that all faces in the room appeared indistinguishable. She was fully aware of the locations of faces and even the presence of specific facial features and denied any other alterations of perceptual experience. She was able to correctly describe alterations made to observers' faces, e.g., removal of spectacles or placing red rectangular tape on the cheek of one observer."

In these results, the study team saw support for a sort of holistic theory of face recognition: "This is unequivocal evidence that prosopagnosia can be attributed to a discrete cortical region and is not directly related to other disturbances in visual function. In addition … the cortical localization of featural processing [i.e., the recognition of individual facial features] appears to be distinct from the stimulated region which is critical for face discrimination." It seems that we do not perceive a turned-up nose, a full, impish smile, a sweeping jawline, darkly arching brows, and gradually put it all together before recognizing *my cousin Shelley*. We recognize or do not recognize in a flash, taking the entire face in and treating it as an irreducible percept.

How does such complex processing take place all at once? Further measurements indicated that the brain may be comparing any particular face to a stored template or standard face that has been built up from experience. The processing, which might be thought of as a subtraction of each face from the template, is quick but not instantaneous, apparently taking from 0.15 to 0.20 seconds. Milton and colleagues came to those conclusions not by stimulating electrode No. 24, but by taking a closer look at the evoked potentials on the electrode as the patient was suddenly presented with images of different faces. Unfamiliar faces produced the quickest and strongest deflections of the potential. Progressively slower and weaker responses were generated by the faces of the patient's physician, her mother and electronically "averaged" constructions that smeared together the features of many people. Still less vigorous responses followed images that were harder to recognize as such—grainy pictures or fragments showing half a face or just a pair of eyes.

For an image that is manifestly a face, the greater the deviation from a norm based on experience and familiarity, the stronger the response based on the evoked potential of electrode No. 24. After the tests, the patient had major brain surgery in hopes of suppressing both the seizures and the auras. "She's doing pretty well," one of the team members told me by phone the other day. For the first time in her life, she is able to hold a steady job in her chosen field, nursing. Occasionally, early in the morning, she experiences slight, unexplained distortions of familiar objects like the knobs on a television set. By and large, she is, thankfully, leading a normal life, her former existence having bequeathed to the world one answer to the question of how much of us is switchboard and how much is spirit and whether there is any essential difference at all.

> *green foothills two weeks the spring two weeks we climbed we clambered dry months came two weeks green foothills brown months dry months the chinook brought fires over the ridge at night like floating red hair we climbed two weeks the spring we climbed we clambered the chinook the trees went up like roman candles green foothills dry months brown months the chinook brought fires red hair we climbed the spring two weeks green foothills*

One passage from "The Terminal Man" has remained stuck in my memory since I read it in high school, a remembered image that still sparks an electric wiggle of response at the least provocation. Leafing now through a copy of the book that is due at the city library on APR 23 1999 (as sloppily stamped on the circulation card below 18 other dates beginning with SEP 29 1997), I see that in the pages leading up to that passage, a surgical team is stimulating electrodes in Harry Benson's brain—the routine task of mapping out areas of functionality. A technological whiz named Gerhard pushes a button to stimulate electrode No. 1 and Benson tastes a ham sandwich. Gerhard stimulates electrode No. 2 and Benson feels that he has to go to the bathroom. As the procedure wears on, Gerhard's mind wanders. He recalls when, early in his career, he requested a brain to dissect. With a stack of neuroanatomy texts to guide him, Gerhard remembers, he scraped and scraped and scraped until the brain had been frittered away to nothing.

Crichton's intent is to illustrate the density, the complexity, the mystery of the brain. Myself, I have always been tempted to see in that empty dissection table the fruitless end of any purely scientific search for human quiddity. *Il suo cervello svapora*—the Italian way of saying that one is worn out mentally, one needs a vacation. Literally, "one's brain evaporates." Of course, we have more than the glories of science to lead us to the dewy essence of ourselves, and we should follow those other meadow paths with equal passion, equal tenacity. This morning I purchased a Grateful Dead CD. It was a new experience for me. Once, long ago—long before I collided with the Deadhead along the lake—a car with the Colorado license plate SUGRE ran me down as I rode my bicycle to work. The impact was a glancing one, and although the bicycle slid under the wheels of the car and was mangled, I suffered no more than a fall. What stunned me more than the impact was sitting on the asphalt and watching the word SUGRE recede as the car sped away. I heard a car door open and slam shut behind me. A very concerned woman appeared in my field of view. She asked if I was all right, then assured me that the hit-and-run driver would certainly be caught, because his vanity plates were based on the famous Grateful Dead song called "Sugaree."

The plates turned out to be stolen. The driver was never caught. Hoping somehow to complete the synaptic circle of association, I bought a CD with that song on it, but the late Garcia, who is apparently the vocalist, mumbles a lot, and the lyrics are far from revelatory. As a hedge, however, I also bought a CD by the band called Grand Mal, whose offerings were of course right next to those of the Grateful Dead in the store. *All the girls and boys / Are like wind-up toys / Like broken machines*, shout the Anglophone members of Grand Mal, and I can work with that. What we have here, aside from inept trochaic trimeter, is an exaggeration of Cartesian dualism in which the observers in their intense threnody consider that only they have escaped the mathematical limit of complete soullessness. This stance recalls the stories, whether accurate or not, of Cartesian vivisectionists laughing at the agony of cats under examination, since their screams were regarded as nothing more than the sounds of damaged machines grinding to a halt. Well, I don't agree.

Like a good experimentalist, I have been keeping a close eye on my own yellow cat. Today it was rolling around on its back in a bar of sunlight, licking its paws and batting at the fat, charcoal cat, apparently as content as could be. The yellow cat has four or five seizures a year. For days or weeks after each one, it avoids the room in which the seizure occurred, except to slink about in search of something it seems to believe is hiding in there. Unlike the charcoal cat, which scratches at its own reflection in the closet mirrors and seems to make a game of staring at people in them, the yellow cat showed no interest in that other world until, one day, after a particularly violent seizure, it froze in front of the expanse of glass, terrified of its own wide-eyed reflection. I had to pick the cat up and move it. Soon it again lost interest in reflections.

Steven Schiff and I have continued the correspondence that began sometime after the day we spent talking about controlling chaos in a dish. He remains stonily unimpressed by my cat observations, but is always available to discuss the latest academic and clinical research on the rhythms of the brain. When it comes to the crazy firing of epilepsy, Schiff is lately intrigued by the ideas of a mathematician named Predrag Cvitanovic, who has shown that the shortest (meaning the briefest) unstable periodic orbits of any system reveal the most about its underlying structure. It is as if, in some sort of "Tommy" scenario, you wanted to reconstruct a three-bumper pinball machine just by listening to a few games. The fleeting periodicity of the ball rattling between two or more of the bumpers would tell you more than a distant rebound off one of the walls. In the epileptic brain, the configuration of the bumpers might correspond to a damaged and otherwise unknowable pattern of connections among the neurons themselves.

Those ideas, like stochastic resonance, chaos and bistability, should also have a story to tell about the intricate rhythms of the healthy brain, which on a very quiet day might sound more like a 100-story arcade of interrelated video games, dart boards, pinball machines, bowling alleys and basketball courts all being used at once and heard from half a mile away. The question of how some or all of those rhythms are linked, correlated, mutually dependent at any moment is in fact a central one. What binds together our disparate perceptions and thoughts and motor responses into a coherent whole? How would either invasive probes (electrodes) or noninvasive ones (magnetic fields generated by electrical currents in the cortex and measured extracranially; positron emission tomography; functional magnetic-resonance imaging) uncover that coherence if they were monitoring various regions of the brain?

Grasping those correlations will likely require a far deeper understanding of the brain than called upon in studies of solitary rhythms, no matter how complicated. A new and more encompassing notion of synchrony itself might be needed. Rather than audible rhythms, Schiff asks me to imagine barefoot children playing together on a beach. The diagnostics, whatever they are, record only the footprints. If some of the children are walking together in a tidy row, then ordinary mathematics ought to be capable of picking out those footprints and determining that they are correlated, coordinated. But what if some of the children are building a city of sandcastles, having a game of tag or playing hide-and-go-seek in the dunes along the beach? How could anyone read the pattern of their footprints if the children drift between all three activities among thousands of other beach-goers who are creating their own footprints while walking dogs, flying kites, chasing Frisbees, playing volleyball, searching for a sunny opening in the crowd and folding out lounge chairs?

Yet the children are on the beach. They are building sandcastles and hiding in the dunes. There is mystery walking barefoot upon the sands of human consciousness.

James Glanz received his Ph.D. from Princeton University and is currently a writer at Science magazine. His work has appeared in a wide range of publications from the New York Times to Astronomy Magazine.

Scrambled Eggs

Marilyn A. Gelman

*L*ife goes on after brain injury. Not like before. Not like you would have imagined, even if you could imagine it happening to you. Not in a clean, safe, nourishing environment. Not with your needs met. Not with the same tastes, smells, thoughts. Not with time out for a family wedding or cancer.

You inhabit a body you do not recognize, driven by someone else's mind that limps down the highway of life with three tires on four wheels. Your scar-free chassis mocks your shattered working parts. No road map shows the way.

Because you desperately wish to conjure the familiar from the usual, against the laws of common sense, you keep trying to cook. Until tasting, you think you have combined the same ingredients.

The final product lacks your spice of life.

Pot Roast
October 12, 1997

Pre-preparation

Three years before you want to prepare Pot Roast The Way It Used To Be, you incur a brain injury on the way home from work when another person makes a foolish left turn into your car.

Ingredients

Chopped onions—a small plastic storage bagful that Mary, the chore-service worker, cut up two days before. Mary spends three hours one week with you and two hours the next, and so you must plan how much chopping to assign her in one visit. You must leave the kitchen while she works because the sound disables you.

Lean top of the rib—from the butcher, delivered two days ago, on the day he delivers to your town, and souring, but you cannot resupply at will. You do not get out to shop, so you have lost the seasons. Are peaches plentiful now, or apples? Are matzohs on display, or candy canes?

Crisco brand shortening

Boiling water—not really at a rolling, vigorous boil the way you would like, but at the best you can manage safely under the circumstances.

Potatoes—the plastic bagful that Mary peeled and cubed two days before, now multicolored. You would have preferred to cook when the potatoes were white, the onions crisp, and the meat not on the cusp of spoiled, but just having Mary softly walking about and doing chores is too much stimulation for you.

You had worked all evening before and all morning preparing lists for her. There are supermarket items, bank chores, post office instructions, and bags for the dry-cleaner and the library. But there is no second chance. Whatever you omit must wait until next week. When she leaves, you must rest or risk injury by falling or crashing into the walls or dropping things on your foot. You've already made two emergency-room visits for fingers smashed under similar circumstances of overload and exhaustion.

Procedure

1. Place a heaping tablespoon of Crisco shortening in a big pot. It is good finally to use the pot again. Because you cannot manage to get the pot to and from its storage place, it has been sitting on top of the stove, collecting dust, for months. Pick up the shortening can after you drop it upside down. Try to discount the buzzing in your ears and the slight feeling of dizziness and nausea produced by the sight and sound of the flying, crashing can. You jumped away well.

2. Turn on stove.

3. Bend down to retrieve the bag of diced onions from the bottom shelf of the refrigerator. The onions cost you a great deal of

money because Mary gets a fair hourly wage for her labors; she is a very good, precise worker. Most of the onions are the same size and thickness, and she diced all three as you had requested. But you forgot that you stuffed the bottom shelf with food that arrived at a later date, and the onion bag had been shoved to the rear.

You were uncertain about the amount of food you would receive from a charitable organization the day between the dicing and the cooking. The new food is in a large paper bag, enclosed in a larger plastic bag; only the bottom shelf would meet its "easy-to-find-later" positional requirement. The bag of charity food is heavy; when you stooped to store it in the refrigerator, your neck cramped, your arm felt numb, and you became dizzy and nauseated. So you rushed the task, and the plastic bag of onions lost its place.

A plastic tab slides across the top of the onion bag to seal it securely, and the bag itself is expensive. No onions will spread throughout the refrigerator in a wild dash for freedom or drop to the floor while the bag is in transit to the stove. It will be a shame to toss the bag out after only one use, but the noise and sight of the running water required to rinse it out will contribute to your general sensory overload at food-preparation time. The mental effort to remember to wash it out later would cost more than the financial gain accrued in saving the bag.

Now, foraging around the bottom shelf of the refrigerator consumes a great deal of your internal resources and pushes you closer to mishaps.

4. Brown the onions on medium heat. The noise of the sizzling onions will increase your dizziness and disorient you. You will lose your ability to distinguish distance and so burn the inside of your right forearm on the side of the hot pot.

You must stand close to the pot of onions because you cannot smell them burning; you cannot take your hearing problems away from the fire. You try to distract yourself by unloading the dishwasher. Since you are addled already, a little more bending and stretching should not make a difference.

As soon as you open a cabinet door, a flying box of coffee filters grazes your head. Even though you have not used the pile of pink china dishes on the right side of the most accessible cabinet since the

BMW hit your Chevrolet, you have been unable to move them to a quieter spot in the kitchen. The dishes take up one of the few places you could store things you use every day, and the coffee-filter box was balanced so precariously on top of the soup plates that it assaulted you at the first opportunity.

Unfortunately, you cannot delay the pot roast. You are at risk because Tuesday's meat and potatoes are becoming the worse for wear. Unexpected fresh produce rots in a box on the kitchen floor, over the furnace as it happens, because there is no room in the refrigerator until the meat and plastic bag of potatoes are removed.

5. Wash the meat and season it with garlic powder and onion powder.

6. Stand far back from the stove. Position yourself so that the pot of burning onions will not reach you if the meat lands in the wrong place; lob the meat into the pot; sear it over a high flame.

Remember to remain in the kitchen at all times, so the noise of the cooking meat can feel like little electric shocks. You are safe until you have to turn the meat. You will have to figure out how to hold the pot, and you must enforce your decision with deliberate and exacting thinking.

Even though you are in the kitchen and can hear the meat sizzling, you cannot smell progress. Periodically evaluate the color of the smoke rising from the pot to determine when to flip the slab of meat. Safe again, until it is time to add water.

While the meat cooks, receive two telephone calls from a man who wrote you a letter and seems to be masturbating. Call the police and hit *57 to trace future calls. Call friend to discuss anxiety and guilt over guy masturbating over phone. Rehash a form that has been haunting you for weeks. The form is for Meals on Wheels; if you could make phone calls and leave messages, it would have been off your plate after one or two chews. But it persists, tough to swallow and often reheated.

You must not get distracted. Back to the pot roast.

The secret to this recipe is the temperature of the water that you will add to the pot once the meat is browned all over and cooked through. The water must be boiling.

You have not boiled water in a whistling kettle on top of the stove since you wrapped your right hand around the body of the kettle to move it off a burner when it was very hot. You have been boiling water in the microwave oven. It never quite gets to that vigorous rolling boil you remember from before, and steam does not rise up as you pour the water out. But now, you are lucky. The two-cup Pyrex measuring cup is clean and ready, and you put tap water in this and put the cup into the microwave. Fortunately the microwave rings a bell when the appointed time has been spent, and shuts itself off, because you have forgotten that you have put the water in the microwave.

7. Carry the cup of boiling water from the microwave, and pour it into the pot containing the hot onions and the sizzling meat. If you manage this task safely, and remember to lower the light on the pot, you must try your very best to stay awake for an hour or so. The effort and the sensory stimulation of the flying Crisco can and coffee-filter box, the sizzling onions, and the scary boiling water march exhaust you. You worry that you will fall asleep, or that you will be in another room and forget the stove is on.

You try to stay in the kitchen, but there is not much you can do. You are in no shape to wash the grime off the refrigerator, or water the little plants on the windowsill that look so thirsty, or polish anything you have missed touching for so long. Sometimes cleaning things is like making love to them, and you haven't been able to dust, polish, or shine since the crash.

It is difficult to tell if the pot roast is the same as the one your mother, then you, used to make. Nothing tastes quite right since the collision, on the lawn of the Maywood, New Jersey, Bon Buffet restaurant three years ago, scrambled everything you knew to be true.

Making a Meat Loaf
1998

Pre-preparation

As a passenger in a car that gets hit, exacerbate injuries from four years ago, add new ones; wait six months; try to cook again.

Part One: Salivate

1. Do not make any telephone calls or write anything demanding

of mental attention, or bend or stretch, in order to maintain optimal functioning.

2. Have ready in advance: 2 lbs. chopped meat, 1 chopped onion, already-opened jar of marinara sauce.

Part Two: Machinate

1. Move stuff away from oven door; reach up to get matches; reach down to light oven.

2. Move portable dishwasher away from pantry door because first glance on shelf did not reveal meat-loaf pan that was in clear, easily accessible location.

3. Bend for pan; reach for oatmeal; replace dishwasher.

4. Bend for marinara sauce in refrigerator; reach for chopped onions; swivel for marinara sauce.

5. Reach for bowl in Hoosier cabinet.

6. The world is spinning already.

Part Three: Activate

1. Break and mix up egg; add oatmeal and marinara sauce. Mix. Get dizzy and nauseous.

2. Add chopped meat; mix with other ingredients; find another, larger fork because there is too much action for so little mixing.

3. Close eyes while working; right shoulder feels funny and center of back of neck hurts. Keep mixing.

4. Pour meat-loaf into pan and shape with two forks. Pour some marinara sauce over top from jar that is now only one-third full. But it feels very heavy. Smooth sauce over top of meat-loaf carefully because fork is hard to keep a grip on; muscles lack coordination.

5. Reach into bottom of refrigerator for sweet potatoes since they are known to be in refrigerator, having been placed there last night in a convenient location for today, now completely forgotten. Difficult to focus on task at hand; wash sweet potatoes. If phone were to ring now, answering machine would do all the work because you do not think your lips would work the words correctly.

6. Carry oh-so-heavy meat-loaf pan to oven and sweet potatoes. Shelf is up a rung too high. You are too uncoordinated now to move it; you would only get hurt or drop something or react poorly to an emergency.

Part Four: Ruminate

You are astonished at how much functionality you have lost. You have pain across the shoulder blades and in the back of the neck; your vision has become less ... cooperative (? you can't think of the word); your head is spinning; feels like your fingers are swollen; your tongue feels swollen; your left ear feels funny on the outside (like it is swelling). Even sitting still with your eyes closed, you are overwhelmed by sensory overload. It is a terrible struggle to type this; you have made and corrected many typos; you have changed many words because you *ca not* think of the right ones; and you fear falling off the chair. You don't want to lie down now, but you had better. And you bet the room will spin while you are lying in bed, and you will see light flashing on and off within your closed eyelids, and you hope no one you need to speak to telephones you today because you will not be able to do whatever it is you would have had to do if they called (this whole phrase is unnecessary, but you are unable to find a word to follow "able to.") Your back and your arms hurt, and you are yawning.

So much for today. It is over as far as you are concerned, and all the rest of the day will be an atte

Marilyn A. Gelman's *work has appeared in the New York Times, Modern Romances and Footwork: The Paterson Literary Review. Before a BMW hit her Chevrolet, she was a graduate student, wrote software, folk-danced, took guitar lessons, attended Mensa events and indulged her great curiousity about everything.*

Romancing

the Brain

F7-T3

T3-T5

T5-O1

PITTSBURGH CENTER FOR THE ARTS

FP1-F3

Artists

Colby Caldwell Justine Cooper
Katharina Fritsch **Alice Hargrave**
Gary Hill Shirley Klinghoffer
Mark Mennin **Jann Rosen-Queralt**
Todd Siler Michael Spano
David Webster **Gail Wight**

Thanks to the artists in the show for their creative reflections and to the lenders for their generosity:
Colby Caldwell; Carol Ehlers Gallery, Ltd.; Ronald Feldman Fine Arts; Alice Hargrave; Shirley Klinghoffer;
Matthew Marks Gallery; Mark Mennin; Jann Rosen-Queralt; Todd Siler; Michael Spano; Howard Stein;
David Webster; Thea Westreich of Art Advisory Services; and Gail Wight.

Introduction   Laura Willumsen
EXECUTIVE DIRECTOR

This seminal exhibition is the brainchild of guest curator Suzanne Ramljak, who proposed the idea after visiting *Recycling Art History* at the Center last year. Drawing on a rich variety of interdisciplinary sources, Ramljak has articulated our culture's love affair with the brain, the physical center of self, imagination, pain, learning, emotions, and behavior. The artists in the show brilliantly interpret this complex topic, melding the reflections of psychologists, neurologists, and philosophers. Ramljak has worked in e-counterpoint over many long months with our own Vicky Clark to capture the essence of this near-infinite topic, maintaining a broad yet finely-tuned aesthetic perspective.

Romancing the Brain has led to two new and timely collaborations. *Creative Nonfiction,* a nationally distributed literary journal based in Pittsburgh, devoted its entire fall issue to the subject of the brain, and will include this catalogue within its covers. The Carnegie Science Center premieres *Gray Matters: The Brain Movie* in September, an interactive exhibit jointly designed by a team of scientists and artists. Thanks to support from the Pennsylvania Humanities Council, this collaboration has led to three panel discussions delving more deeply into this mysterious and endlessly fascinating neuro-turf.

Acknowledgements

Our special thanks go to Suzanne Ramljak for her work which includes her insightful essay and her interview with Barbara Maria Stafford, professor of Art History at the University of Chicago and author of *Body Criticism: Imaging the Unseen in Enlightenment Art and Medicine (1993).* We are grateful for the contribution to the catalogue by Dr. Michael Salcman, a neurosurgeon, neuroscientist and poet who writes frequently on the arts and sciences. The uninhibited talent of co-sponsor Wall-to-Wall Studios has made for a delightful first collaboration. The show is possible because of the generous financial support of TR Services and Single Point Systems, and because of wonderful coverage by our media sponsor, the *Pittsburgh Post-Gazette.*

Michael Spano *Brain with Membrane* (Brain Research Laboratory, Reed Institute, UCLA), 1998
Gelatin silver print, 50 x 40" COLLECTION OF THE ARTIST, BROOKLYN

F7-T3

Interview Desperately Seeking

▶ Suzanne Ramljak:

How would you characterize our culture's current
involvement with the brain? Is it purely scientific
or more akin to a romance?

Suzanne Ramljak's EEG report CONDUCTED BY DR. RICHARD LECHTENBERG (see above) by Suzanne Ramljak

Romancing the Brain

At first blush, romance and the brain may seem an unlikely pair, but the metaphor of romantic love proves to be apt for capturing our culture's relationship with the brain. Within the fields of science, art, and popular culture there is ample evidence to suggest that the human brain has become our new object of desire. This increasing cultural fascination is borne out by the works in *Romancing the Brain,* which offer an opportunity to ponder the passionate involvement we are having with a captivating 3-pound mass of tissue.

Neural Relations

Barbara Maria Stafford:

Our culture's relationship with the brain is an obsession that has, at a deep level, to do with control. We hear so much today about chemical intervention versus psychiatry, brain localization for drug treatment, etc., and I don't think that these issues are about romance. Rather, it is the specter, or utopia, of behavioral micro-control at the neuronal level.

Scientific research has often been compared to a great love affair or the courtship of an elusive muse. Any successful romance requires an element of mystery, and the mysterious is also inherent in the scientific pursuit. The central role of enigma in science was recognized by Albert Einstein who observed, "The fairest thing we can experience is the mysterious. It is the fundamental emotion which stands at the cradle of true art and true science." [1] Such an attraction to the unknown is especially keen for artists and scientists engaged with the brain, which has rightly been called the "most complicated material object in the known universe." [2]

The quest to unlock the mysteries of the human brain has fueled the growth of an entire brain industry and millions of dollars are spent on neuroscientific research each year. With a determination bordering on obsession, scientists are striving to pinpoint neurological triggers for everything from suicide to snoring. The skull's bony vault—which encases its precious tissue like a chastity belt—has not deterred researchers, and the brain is daily sliced, probed, radiated, and photographed in the hopes that it will yield its secrets. Like the freshly exposed gray matter in Michael Spano's laboratory photographs, the brain now lies naked and vulnerable under our gaze.

Katharina Fritsch *Gehim (Brain), 1987/89*
Plaster of Paris, paint, 4 1/2 x 5 7/8 x 5 1/8" COURTESY MATTHEW MARKS GALLERY, NEW YORK
©1999 ARTIST'S RIGHTS SOCIETY (ARS), NEW YORK/VG BILD-KUNST, BONN

Interview

FP1-F7

F7-T3

▶ SR: As the Decade of the Brain draws to a close, do you think we have made great strides in our understanding of the brain and its functions?

[The mysterious] is the fundamental emotion which stands at the cradle of true art and true science. — ALBERT EINSTEIN

BMS: An enormous amount of work has been done on determining the functional properties of differing areas of the brain by altering its neurophysiology and neurochemistry. What has not been figured out is what is the connection between a materialist, computer-driven neurophysiology and old-fashioned psychology. We still need a unified understanding of physiological and mental processes.

Shirley Klinghoffer *Animal, Vegetable, Mineral,* 1993
Bronze, glass, 39 x 24 x 19" COLLECTION OF THE ARTIST, NEW YORK

Interview

▶ SR: In spite of the new research findings,
do you think that science still operates with old,
even outmoded, paradigms of the brain?

Of course, artists have long been engaged in the process of exposing and probing the human body. Dissection and anatomy have been staples of artistic training from the 14th to the early 20th century, and Leonardo da Vinci even developed a technique for drilling and pouring wax into the brain's ventricles to obtain a cast of its contours. The ability to envision and map the body's interior has radically advanced during the twentieth century in the wake of scientific discoveries like the X-ray in 1895. The last two decades have witnessed the rapid rise of anatomical depiction due to new medical technologies like magnetic resonance imaging (MRI), computerized axial tomography (CAT) and positron emission tomography (PET) scans. But while the brain is now more visually accessible than ever, it has not become any less inscrutable.

Our cultural infatuation with the brain and related fields such as consciousness studies has now reached a state that could even be called fetishistic. Like a fetish, the brain has become an object of extreme reverence, one invested with exorbitant value. In Freudian psychology, a fetish is a substitute for a missing object (the mother's absent phallus) and as such serves to compensate us for a psychic loss. Within this context, the brain-as-fetish could be seen as a surrogate object for a lost sense of selfhood. The Freudian fetish is essentially defined by its potential for sexual arousal and gratification, and the brain's long-standing status as the most erotic organ in the human body has only been confirmed by recent research.

BMS: I think there remains a neuronal dualism in place, a neo-Cartesianism, that forgets that the brain and brain function are part of the body. The dichotomy between intellect and flesh is even more exacerbated now as scientific discussions focus on various signals, circuits, and mechanisms of synaptic change. We need to get the functions of neurons together with that of symbols and culture. I find it exciting, however, that 19th-century concepts like synesthesia are making a comeback in certain scientific quarters because researchers are becoming more interested in the concurrence of the senses.

At the center of any romantic liaison is physical love and intimate engagement. Likewise, the neurological romance playing out in our culture has led to a closer involvement with the fleshy, carnal nature of the brain. The brain's materiality is made explicit in the work of artists such as Katharina Fritsch, Shirley Klinghoffer, Mark Mennin and Gail Wight who address the dual nature of the brain as a material object and the obscure source of consciousness. The old Cartesian dualism—which held that the mind and body are separate entities—has been firmly challenged with new biological research, which underscores the mind's inescapable ties to the flesh. A strong advocate for this view, neuroscientist Gerald Edelman, counters the notion of a disembodied mind with a "biologically based epistemology" that regrounds the brain's processes in bodily functions.[3] Immersing brain activity even further in the body's depths, neurobiologist Michael Gershon has posited a "second brain" in our bowel, an intestinal nervous system that operates independently of the brain or spinal cord.[4]

Recent neuroscientific findings coincide with yet another feature of the romantic experience— the role of subjectivity in our perception. Art has long been a bastion of subjectivity and has served as the best record of human individuality and sensibility. The natural alliance between artistic endeavor and theories of the subjective brain has been asserted by Gerald Edelman

Gail Wight *Honey,* 1999 (detail)
Glass jar, human brain, honey, radio, steel base, infrared detectors, 48 x 30 x 30" COLLECTION OF THE ARTIST, SAN FRANCISCO

Interview

▶ SR: You have written about how modes of visualization shape our understanding, along the lines of Marshall McLuhan's dictum "the medium is the message." What role do medical imaging technologies play in defining our understanding of the human brain?

The neurological romance playing out in our culture has led to a closer involvement with the fleshy, carnal nature of the brain.

BMS: One of the most important things to remember in scientific imaging technologies, if not the most important thing, is that no one technology gives you all the properties of the observed object. PET, MRI, CAT scans all map a particular, distinctive object property. But no imaging technology provides the total picture. That's why there's such a drive now to superimpose different imaging modalities. Artists and art historians could help enormously by drawing attention to the importance of various formats and genres within such images and the very different results of this compositional variety. We need to distinguish the diverse imaging formats, especially in light of the tendency of electronic media to converge and morph all pictures into a hyper-illusionary meld.

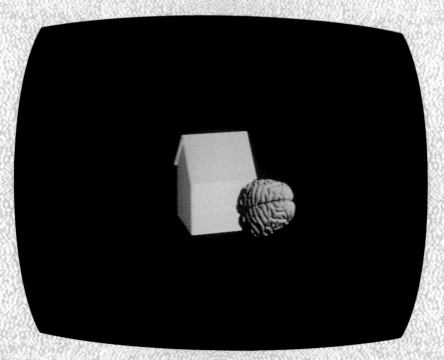

Gary Hill *Liminal Object #2*, 1996 (detail)
Single-channel video installation, monitor, laserdisc player, metal stand and laser disc COLLECTION THEA WESTREICH, NEW YORK
PHOTO: COURTESY BARBARA GLADSTONE GALLERY, NEW YORK

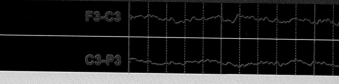

Interview

▶ SR: Given that artists and scientists are both engaged
in a quest to visualize the unseen, how would you
compare these two modes of inquiry?

who sees the brain functioning according to a process of biological selectionism from "vast and diverse neural repertoires, [which] gives each brain its unique shape" and can "account for the individuality of our responses."[5] The dense complexity of these neural networks is conveyed in Todd Siler's *Neurosphere* and in the montage light boxes of Jann Rosen-Queralt.

In spite of advances in neuroscience, the brain still remains an organ steeped in obscurity. As the Decade of the Brain draws to a close, the most basic questions about the human brain are left unanswered: how do we remember; why do we dream; what are emotions; what does it mean to be conscious; how is it that we can even think at all? Researchers have only begun to explore such questions and this early stage in our quest to map the brain has justly been compared to Columbus's first voyage across the sea. The journey is made even more difficult by the fact that the object of this pursuit is also the pursuer. With brain research we are engaged in a form of cerebral tail chasing, as our minds attempt to comprehend the brain, which in turn sustains the processes of our mind. As Eastern philosopher Alan Watts put it, trying to define yourself is like trying to "bite your own teeth."[6] The elusiveness of this quest to become conscious of our brains is visualized in Gary Hill's *Liminal Object #2*, featuring a video loop of a brain and house.

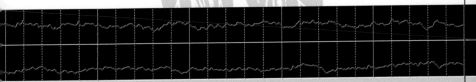

BMS: I think we are witnessing the emergence of a neuronal aesthetic. Composition is a great point of comparison: it externalizes the invisible nomenal in the visible phenomenal. Line, color, orientation, vectors, shading, all produce certain emotional responses that are simultaneously rule-bound and conventional. These compositional mechanisms and their calculable effects on the beholder engaged a wide spectrum of artist-theorists from Humbert de Superville to Piet Mondrian. Also, artists and medical researchers today might possibly agree that computation and measurement are not where the most interesting inquiry lies. Obviously, we need technical and physical expertise in order to speak about an embodied experience, but one that also involves perception, tact, judgment.

In spite of the difficulties, our cultural longing to gain a more intimate knowledge of the human brain is the most significant quest of our era. The findings of brain research will not only impact our future health and disease, but will also have a bearing on such crucial issues as human freedom, responsibility, and individuality. In addition to its great cultural import, the romance of the brain is also one of the most poignant relationships in human history. For ultimately our desire to know the brain is a desire to know ourselves, which might be a form of love that remains forever unrequited.

[1] Albert Einstein, "The World as I See It," in *The World as I See It*
(New York: Philosophical Library, 1949) p. 5.

[2] Gerald M. Edelman, "The Wordless Metaphor: Visual Art and the Brain," in Klaus Kertess
et al., *Whitney Biennial* (New York: Whitney Museum of American Art, 1995) p. 36.

[3] Gerald M. Edelman, *Bright Air, Brilliant Fire: On the Matter of the Mind*
(New York: Basic Books, 1992) p. 164.

[4] Michael Gershon, *The Second Brain: The Scientific Basis of Gut Instinct
and a Groundbreaking New Understanding of Nervous Disorders of the Stomach and Intestines* (New York: HarperCollins, 1998)

[5] Edelman, "The Wordless Metaphor: Visual Art and the Brain," p. 47

[6] Alan Watts, *The Book (On the Taboo Against Knowing Who You Are)*
(New York: Collier Books, 1967) p. 15

Alice Hargrave *Fear, Brain MRI*, 1998
Iris print, 15 x 15" COURTESY THE ARTIST AND CAROL EHLERS GALLERY, CHICAGO

P3-O1

Interview

FP2-F4

▶ SR: What is the key concern or question that we should be addressing as we move forward into the brave new world of neuroscience?

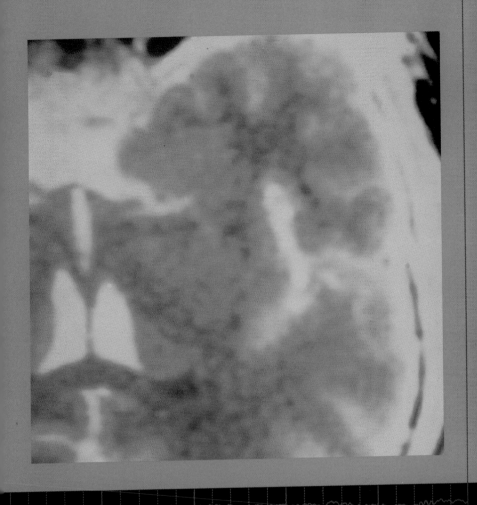

BMS: Unification: How do we tie in neurobiological mechanisms with personae, and social and cultural experience? Also, what are the top-down (cognitive) hard-wired aspects of visual experience and what are the learned aspects? How do different stimuli become synchronized?

Todd Siler *The Neurosphere*, 1992-93 (detail)
Mixed media on synthetic canvas COURTESY THE ARTIST AND RONALD FELDMAN FINE ARTS, NEW YORK
PHOTO: D. JAMES DEE

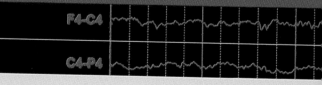

Interview

► SR: Do you see artificial intelligence as a real
option for the future, or does your understanding
of the brain and of consciousness preclude such
a possibility?

BMS: Incredible developments are occurring in Artificial Life. There is now a "neurochip" that uses DNA strands instead of circuitry. Nano-devices appear to be the wave of the future. Artificial intelligence has also evolved towards more "biological" machinery that attempts to model heterogeneous reasoning. But, I agree with the philosopher John Searle, simulation is not duplication.

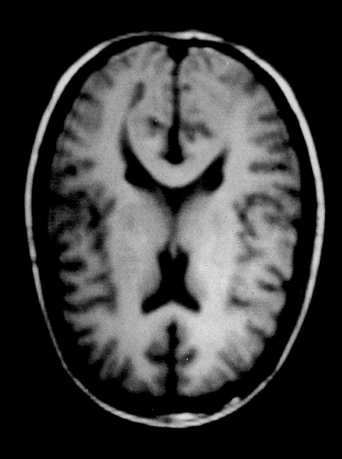

our ability to visualize that which cannot be **(directly)** *seen...*

Colby Caldwell *Untitled, No. 3,* 1997
Waxed and mounted photograph, 24 x 20" COLLECTION OF THE ARTIST, WASHINGTON, D.C.

(Imag)ining
the Brain

by Dr. Michael Salcman

Today neuroscience has many techniques to image the human brain, even while it is awake or dreaming or looking at art. Imagine a horizontal cross section of the brain across which x-rays are beamed, their absorption determined by the relative density of the tissues within. Reconstruct these two-dimensional cross sections on a computer and you have a CAT scan, or computerized axial tomography. Imagine instead that you injected a radioactive drug into the bloodstream, and then measured and mapped the radiation at multiple points on the surface of the skull; you would then have a PET scan, or positron emission tomography. Or, imagine exposing the brain to a magnetic field, orienting the tiny magnets in the hydrogen (proton) carrying molecules, and making a three-dimensional computerized map based on the distribution of magnetic molecules; you would have a MRI scan or magnetic resonance imaging.

And if you combined the information from a CAT, PET, or MRI scan to derive the mathematical coordinates of a tumor or target in the brain and with those calculations drove a probe or a microscope into the brain's depths, you would have modern neurosurgery, a contemporary marriage of art and science based on our ability to visualize that which cannot be directly seen. If you further produced color-coded pictures of the brain in which levels of mental activity, blood flow and metabolism were simultaneously displayed across a spectrum of hues, you would have something scientific that looked very much like art, and it would even save lives.

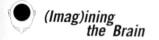

Of course, art has often looked like science and has looked after science, its images and procedures shaped by the culture in which the artist lives. This has been true even when thinkers, most famously C.P. Snow, have believed the languages of art and science mutually incomprehensible. That this is demonstrably false was proven by some of the pioneers of body-centered art—including Leonardo da Vinci and Thomas Eakins—and by the many contemporary scientists who have a profound appreciation for art. Although the artifacts produced by art and science are frequently dissimilar, the behaviors exhibited by artists and scientists are often the same. Both are engaged in a humanistic search for meaning and the success of that search depends on deductive reasoning, independence, experiment, and personal integrity. At present, the external aspects of artifacts produced by art and science appear to be converging; this is especially evident in the appropriation of MRI and CAT scans by artists such as Alice Hargrave, Colby Caldwell and Justine Cooper.

Successive developments in the visual arts—from Renaissance single-point perspective, to Cubism, to conceptual art—have paralleled contemporaneous changes in physics, cosmology, and our understanding of the human body. Much of the change in

*The external **(aspects)** of art and science appear to be converging.*

20th-century art and science occurred under the pressure of the dominant paradigm of the Einsteinian universe, a model invented by a scientist whose primary methodology was inherently artistic. Time, as both a dimension of the universe and a coordinate in our lives, entered artistic practice in the form of happenings, earthworks, performance art and other works that moved or suffered decay. It is hardly surprising, therefore, that artists should now turn their attention to the brain just when molecular neurobiology has supplanted physics as the cutting edge of science.

If, according to Alexander Pope, it is certain that the proper study of mankind is man, then the ultimate study of man must be the organ of our humanity. Plunge a knife into the brain and it does not feel pain, the better it seems to monitor the outside world.

Justine Cooper *Self-Portrait,* 1998
MRI scans, clear film on perspex, 13 ³/₄ x 11 ³/₄ x 11 ³/₄" COLLECTION HOWARD STEIN, NEW YORK
PHOTO: COURTESY JULIE SAUL GALLERY, NEW YORK

If the proper study of mankind is man then the ultimate study of man must be the **(organ)** of our humanity.

— *Alexander Pope*

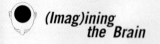

Into the enormous switching network of the brain, consisting of approximately a trillion cells, messages from the outside world are delivered by some 6 million telephone lines, a million of which comprise each optic nerve. Furthermore, one half of the cranial nerves are devoted to moving the eye, working the pupil, keeping the cornea moist and the lens dust free! To virtually all other creatures, the world is viewed flat from the side of the head, seen in a range of gray tonalities. Like primates and birds, we have binocular vision, and we see in stereoscope and in color. We are a species notorious for our sensitivity to coloration and appearance in sexual display, and the brain is our highest erotic organ.

The brain is also the organ of death; the survival of the self does not depend on the heart or lungs. The medical definition of death as the cessation of brain function has been adopted into law. As conscious entities we are completely defined by the gelatinous goo contained within the skull, that traditional component of the memento mori. And the brain begins to die in early adult life with the loss of several thousands of neurons a day. Since its operations are based on the probabilistic interactions of countless cells (see the paintings of David Webster) and the redundant fractal organization of its fibers and circuits, degradation of the brain's performance is difficult to detect short of frank disease. After adolescence the brain has little capacity for plasticity and repair other than the functional consequences of redundancy, or the large number of cells and circuits that perform similar functions. However, damage or destroy enough neural tissue and some functional capabilities are lost for good. But it is now possible to grow a neuron on a silicon chip where it will form a proper electrical connection, and we can direct the growth of fetal cells in

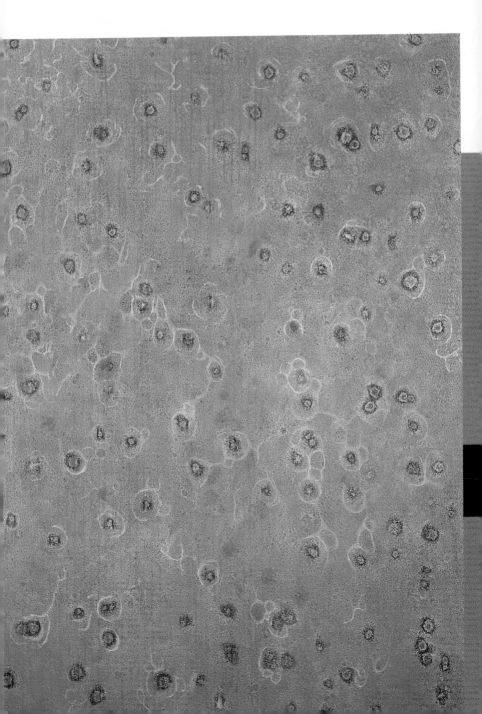

(Imag)ining the Brain

laboratories to produce neurons and neurotransmitters that can be implanted into the brain for the purposes of repair and regeneration. So what does it mean to say that an organ capable of devising such solutions to formerly intractable problems is limited in its plasticity?

At the most simplistic and personal level, the artist and the scientist seek to achieve their own immortality through the creation of works that will outlive them. Art and science are activities that recognize the paradox of the immortal mind trapped within the finitude of the body. Corporeal limitations do not apply to the imagination or the mind, however. Science extends the mind's control over the universe and projects the life of the scientist into the future. Art explores the creation of alternative worlds, writing scripts that are not neccessarily implicit in the physical order. Irrespective of their specific content, art and science are both essentially optimistic programs seeking to extend the life of the individual and the vitality of civilization.

Romancing the Brain: tracking our obsession with the

Exhibition dates:

Credits

GUEST CURATOR: Suzanne Ramljak, New York
DESIGN: Wall-to-Wall Studios, Pittsburgh   PRINTING: Schiff Printing, Pittsburgh   SCANNING: Gamma Graphics, Pittsburgh

Romancing the Brain is co-sponsored by Single Point Systems, TR Services, Wall-to-Wall Studios, and the Pittsburgh Post-Gazette. Public programs have been supported in part by the Pennsylvania Humanities Council, the Federal-State Partner of the National Endowment for the Humanities.

The Center's exhibitions program receives support from generous individuals, the Allegheny Regional Asset District, and jointly from the Pennsylvania Council on the Arts, a state agency, and the National Endowment for the Arts, a federal agency.

Science extends the mind's control over the universe and projects the life of the scientist into the future. Art explores the creation of alternative worlds, writing scripts that are not necessarily implicit in the physical order.

most complex object in the world.

09.18 — 11.21.99

Romancing
the Brain

The Music of the Brain, the Chemistry of the Lute

Ronald Pies

All right, let's be honest. The brain is not a lute, and the six brain chemicals we will discuss are not precisely like the six strings of the lute. But the idea I want to explore—that the chemicals of the brain may be likened to specific musical tones—is not without precedent. The ancient Greeks developed the notion that certain musical modes, or scales, possessed "moral values" that could affect the emotional response of the listener. For example, some modes could activate the individual, while others could undermine mental and spiritual balance. (Plato, in "The Republic" and "The Laws," specifies that only certain kinds of music be played in schools.) While I will not be suggesting such a direct music-to-brain connection—I will not argue, for example, that plucking a specific string of the lute leads to a spritz of serotonin in the brain—I will be presenting a kind of extended metaphor or analogy.

In brief, the brain chemicals underlying mood and behavior relate to one another in roughly the way the strings of a lute interact to produce chords—or, if the instrument is out of tune, discord. Just as one string, when plucked, exerts a harmonic influence on its neighbors, one neurotransmitter in the brain may modify, augment, or counteract another. Just as the lute's strings may be out of tune, the brain's chemistry may be out of balance. But there is another, more literal sense in which the chemicals of the brain may be likened to strings. Several of the major neurotransmitters exert their influence by means of rather long nerve pathways, or "fibers," projecting from one area of the brain to many others. Activating one of these pathways may be likened to plucking a biochemical string. The activating event, of course, is not the musician's finger, but an electrochemical stimulus. This may arise from something external—seeing a Mack truck bearing down on you, for example—or from an internal event, such as a childhood memory or pleasant thought.

There is another aspect of the brain's music that we must understand before proceeding. Just as the strings of a lute may be plucked too loudly or too softly, a particular neurotransmitter pathway may be overactive or underactive—spilling out too much or too little of its chemical messenger. This can have disastrous consequences for mental health and stability, as we will see. But the situation in the brain is quite a bit more complex than this. Nerve cells (neurons) in the brain are covered with microscopic binding sites to which a particular neurotransmitter becomes attached. Once a neurotransmitter latches on to one of these receptors, it sets off a chain of events that leads to activation or suppression of nerve-cell activity. Ultimately, the genetic material of the cell may be subtly altered, leading to production of new proteins or hormones. And just as a string may be tuned too sharp or too flat, neuronal receptors may be abnormally sensitive or insensitive. In response to certain stimuli, these receptors may become more or less sensitive or numerous. In short, there are several ways in which the strings of the brain may become louder or softer, sharper or flatter, depending on the amount and effect of various chemical messengers. Finally, like the strings of the lute, each neurotransmitter pathway may affect its neighbors. When one of these chemical pathways is "plucked" over a long period of time—hours or days, let's say—it may increase or reduce the activity of other pathways. But unlike the vibrations of a string, these neurochemical reverberations often extend over weeks, months, or even years. With our lute analogy in mind, we can now examine some of the principal "strings" of the brain.

Dopamine

Dopamine is the string of fire. Like Prometheus, the Titan who gave fire to mankind, dopamine gives us activation, energy and drive. When the dopamine string is played too softly, we feel lethargic, depressed and "flat." The chemical system that underlies our sense of pleasure and reward is activated by dopamine. Thus, when dopamine is missing, the Beethoven symphony that once excited us now seems like so much elevator music. The sexual partner who once aroused such passion might as well be the old filing clerk at the IRS. Even our movements are slowed without dopamine. In the case of individuals with Parkinson's disease, a critical lack of dopamine leads to profound deficits in movement and motor function. The "parkinsonian" individual is stooped and shuffling, tremulous and unsteady—the consequence of too little dopamine in a part of the brain called the *substantia nigra*. In contrast to all this, the individual with an excessively loud dopamine system may be mad or manic. In schizophrenia, for example, we think that excessive dopamine drives hallucinations and delusions. (On the other hand, some of the so-called negative symptoms of schizophrenia—such as apathy and social withdrawal—may be due to too little dopamine in other regions of the brain.) The individual who has just snorted cocaine is deluged with dopamine. Talk about high-strung: The coke addict is euphoric, overly-energized and hypersexual, at least for a few hours. Sometimes, as in schizophrenia, the cocaine user may become grandiose or paranoid. We think that after many years of cocaine use, the addict's neurons may actually become depleted of dopamine. This withdrawal state can lead to profound depression, lethargy, and somnolence—the infamous "crash" that follows the cocaine binge. Withdrawal, in turn, leads to cocaine craving and further cocaine use, as the addict tries desperately to tune up the slackened dopamine string. A vicious circle of dopamine intoxication and withdrawal often follows. There is some evidence that the manic phase of manic-depressive (bipolar) illness also involves too much noise from the dopamine system; indeed, the manic individual often resembles someone in the midst of cocaine intoxication. Unfortunately, bipolar disorder is driven by its own perverse chords, with bouts of mania and depression alternating over the course of a lifetime.

Serotonin

Serotonin might be called the master string. If dopamine is Promethean, serotonin is surely Protean—after Proteus, the sea-god who could change his shape at will. Serotonin is involved in virtually all aspects of biological function. Sleep, sexuality, aggression, appetite, pain perception, temperature regulation and mood are just a few of serotonin's domains. If you wanted to buy stock in a neurotransmitter, you could do worse than serotonin. Some of the most widely prescribed medications in the world—Prozac, Zoloft, Paxil and others—are essentially agents for amplifying the serotonin string. (In more technical terms, these antidepressants inhibit the mechanism by which serotonin is taken back up into the nerve cell—resulting in more serotonin to communicate with other neurons.)

What happens when the serotonin string is plucked too softly? Like dopamine, serotonin modulates mood. When its volume is too low, people often get depressed. By increasing the amount of serotonin between brain cells, Prozac-type medications can alleviate many cases of depression. (For that matter, so can psychotherapy—and there is every reason to believe that "talk therapy" can affect the chemistry of the brain just as medications can.) More surprising, though, is the connection between low serotonin and aggression. People who tend to be impulsive, violent, or self-destructive seem to have too little serotonin in their central nervous systems—or their serotonin receptors are somehow "tone-deaf" to the neurochemical signal sent out by serotonin neurons. Over the course of many years, these receptors may try to compensate for this weak serotonin signal by becoming more numerous or more sensitive—a process sometimes called *up-regulation*. Paradoxically, what started out as a serotonin deficiency can gradually become a serotonin surplus. Some individuals who wind up with too much serotonin are prone to develop various kinds of anxiety disorders, such as obsessive-compulsive or panic disorder.

Scientists have found that, in such cases, drugs that "tone down" or antagonize serotonin receptors may work as anti-anxiety agents. Oddly enough, Prozac-type medications may also be useful. It may be that by pumping up the volume in the serotonin system, hypersensitive serotonin receptors are gradually able to "down-regulate" back to their original state. All this is just to say that the chemistry of mood is complex and tightly regulated. When the serotonin string is either too soft or too loud, too flat or too sharp, mood and behavior may suffer.

Sleep, appetite and pain are also modulated by serotonin. For example, the serotonin string is quite loud during waking arousal, and virtually silent during a type of sleep called *REM* (for "rapid eye movement"). During REM sleep, which is closely linked with dreaming, the individual's muscle tone is normally very low—probably due to serotonin's silence. This is fortunate, since without suppression of muscle tone, someone dreaming of, say, punching out the boss might act this out upon an innocent bed-partner. (Indeed, in REM sleep behavioral disorder, some people manifest just such violent activity.) Many people who took the now defunct "fen-phen" diet pill may not have realized that serotonin was fundamentally involved in this double agent's action. The "fen" part of the pill was the drug fenfluramine, which boosts serotonin levels in the nervous system. The "phen" part was phenteramine, which is an amphetamine-like stimulant intended to offset fatigue induced by fenfluramine. The good news is that by amplifying the serotonin string, fenfluramine suppresses appetite, and hence, promotes weight loss. The bad news is—as the Food and Drug Administration belatedly realized—that the fen-phen combination seems to cause damage to the valves of the heart. Thus, this agent was removed from the market. Nevertheless, researchers are still interested in the ways in which serotonin may influence appetite and weight. Finally—though the serotonin story could go on for volumes—we know that pain perception is greatly influenced by the serotonin system. For example, people with chronic pain syndromes often benefit from agents that amplify the serotonin signal.

Serotonin does not act independently of other neurotransmitters, of course. When its string sounds, it actually dampens the reverberations of dopamine. This may be part of a subtle homeostatic system in the brain, designed to keep mood and motor activity in careful balance. Unfortunately, it can sometimes lead to unwanted medication side effects, such as the parkinsonian symptoms occasionally seen with Prozac-type antidepressants.

Norepinephrine

Many of us remember the "fight-or-flight" response from high school biology. That Mack truck we mentioned earlier—bearing down on us at 70 miles per hour—evokes a chain of events that equips us either to escape from danger or to confront it head on. We begin to feel our hearts pounding and our breathing increasing in rate

Ronald Pies

and depth. Blood rushes to the muscles of movement, and we are transformed into lean, mean, fighting—or fleeing—machines. One of the chemicals responsible for this fight-or-flight response—-adrenaline, or epinephrine—is produced by the adrenal gland. A close cousin of epinephrine called *norepinephrine* is an important neurotransmitter in the brain. As you might guess, norepinephrine tends to be an *activating* chemical. When its string is plucked, you know it. In fact, excessive norepinephrine in a part of the brain called the *locus ceruleus* may underlie the phenomenon of "panic attacks"—an instance of the fight-or-flight response gone haywire. Some symptoms of mania and post-traumatic stress disorder may also be related to too much noise from the norepinephrine system. On the other hand, when the norepinephrine string is muted or flat, depression may ensue. There is some evidence, for example, that depressed patients have less sensitive norepinephrine receptors than do non-depressed control subjects. (These studies have actually been done on white blood cells, not brain cells, in depressed subjects; however, the receptors are very similar in both types of cells.) It is interesting that after treatment with electroconvulsive therapy (ECT), these norepinephrine receptors achieve normal sensitivity. Since ECT is the most effective treatment known for severe depression, this finding provides evidence that the norepinephrine string may be "flat" in some depressed patients.

GABA, Glutamate, Acetylcholine

Most of the medications that act on mood affect one or more of the three "strings" we have just discussed—dopamine, serotonin, or norepinephrine. However, there are probably scores, if not hundreds, of other neurotransmitters in the human nervous system, each contributing a unique tone to the symphony of mood and behavior. There are three more strings we must discuss here, but these could easily be replaced with others of different tone and timbre.

Two neurotransmitters—GABA and glutamate—remind us of those two contrasting gods in Greek mythology, Apollo and Dionysus. Apollo is usually described as the god of order, light and reason. Dionysus—related to Bacchus, the Roman god of wine—is linked with turbulence, darkness and sensuality. And yet, as Nietzsche

80

taught us in "The Birth of Tragedy," it is the creative tension between the Apollonian and Dionysian that generates the greatest art and drama. In the brain, GABA and glutamate represent opposing neurochemical principles; and yet, their coordinated activity regulates the energy level of virtually every neuron in the brain. GABA—short for gamma aminobutyric acid—is the main inhibitory neurotransmitter in the nervous system. Unlike our previous neurotransmitters (called *biogenic amines*), GABA is an amino acid—a building block of proteins. GABA is ubiquitous in the human central nervous system, with as many as a third of all neurons utilizing GABA as their primary neurotransmitter. If we say that our first three neurotransmitters "fire up" the neuron, we might justifiably say that GABA puts the fire out. When GABA latches on to its receptor site, it causes a flood of negatively charged ions to rush into the neuron, dampening the cell's electrical activity. Repeated over many thousands of neurons, this process seems to underlie behavioral sedation or calmness. When the GABA string sounds, its tone is likely to soothe "the savage breast." Indeed, sedative-hypnotics like Valium and Xanax depend on the activity of GABA for their mechanism of action. When too loud or too insistent, the GABA string may bring on stupor or even coma.

In marked contrast, glutamate is the primary excitatory neurotransmitter in the brain. Glutamate's string sends bold reverberations throughout the brain, awakening the very cells that GABA would put to sleep. Like Dionysus, who could bring madness to those who rejected his divinity, glutamate can bring destruction to the brain, if its activity is too great. Through such excess, neurons can literally be "excited to death." Some data suggest that such "excitotoxicity" underlies the damage seen in stroke and Alzheimer's disease. Ironically—or perhaps quite sensibly in nature's clever economy—glutamate is actually the precursor of GABA. It seems that when neuronal activity gets too intense, the enzyme that converts glutamate to GABA is activated—suggesting that the fine counterpoint between these two contrasting strings provides the brain with a self-regulating calming mechanism. (It is tempting to speculate that in some extraordinarily anxious persons, this enzyme system is somehow defective.)

Finally, our sixth string—acetylcholine. Outside the central nervous system, this neurotransmitter is involved in muscle contraction. (Curare, the poison that brings on muscle paralysis, works by interfering with acetylcholine.) In the brain, acetylcholine is closely involved in memory and higher cognitive functions. When its string is plucked, we can count, calculate and generally sound clever. Individuals with Alzheimer's disease have very low levels of acetylcholine in their brains and, as a consequence, have great difficulty with memory and cognition. Acetylcholine also affects mood. Too loud a tone from this string, and the individual may feel depressed; too soft, and the person may veer toward euphoria or mania. (So-called anticholinergic agents—which interfere with acetylcholine—are actually sold on the streets for their mood-elevating "buzz.") A number of medications for Alzheimer's disease have the effect of restoring brain levels of acetylcholine back to normal.

Chord and Discord in the Music of the Brain

So how do things sound when all six of our strings are played together? How do the chemicals of the brain create the equivalent of chords? What combination of tones leads to discord in brain and behavior? We are a long way from knowing the answers to these questions, but we can make some generalizations. First, it is clear that certain mental illnesses are critically related to abnormalities in one or more of these six neurotransmitters. For example, in schizophrenia, the dopamine string may be too loud in some regions of the brain, while the GABA string may be too soft. This has very direct implications for our treatment of schizophrenia, which normally utilizes drugs that block the dopamine receptor. (Drugs that increase GABA usually have a modest, adjunctive role in treatment.) It is also clear that simple "deficit" theories of mental illness do not do justice to the abnormal brain's cacophony. For example, depression is unlikely to involve simply too little serotonin or norepinephrine. Rather, the amounts of a neurotransmitter, the sensitivity of its receptors, its effects on the gene, and its interactions with many other neurotransmitters may all determine its effects on mood. In the larger arena of temperament or character, we have reason to believe that traits such as shyness or risk-taking may be related to the state of one's neurochemical strings. For example, socially phobic individuals may be deficient in serotonin, while "risk-takers" may have a bit too much dopamine on the brain. (At present, these associations are very tenuous.) Finally, knowing more about the music of the brain may lead us toward ways of enhancing mood, memory and behavior. While human creativity can never be reduced to mere neurotransmitters, we may be able to modulate that creativity by tuning one or more of our strings up or down. Perhaps we can even envision a whole new instrument in which not six, but a hundred strings will play in symphony.

Ronald Pies, M.D., is clinical professor of psychiatry at Tufts University School of Medicine and lecturer on psychiatry at Harvard Medical School. He is the author of a chapbook of poetry, "Riding Down Dark" (Nightshade Press), and a work on comparative religious ethics, "Ethics of the Fathers" (Jason Aronson).

East of Everything

Megan Foss

I

I gained so much weight sitting in jail that my street clothes didn't fit when they released me. I had to wear county-issue jeans and a T-shirt on the airplane I took out of California's Bay area that last time. I returned home to Washington with those jeans and a paper bagful of letters from jail and a Pillow Person my sister bought me at the Target store in Pleasant Hill just before I got released.

I took the Bart train from Concord to the Oakland Airport with $50 in my pocket. There were at least a hundred moments when I started to think about getting off the train and heading back into Bella Vista to cop some heroin. And a hundred times I shut it down. It was like a mantra. *Not an option. Don't turn around. Not an option. Don't turn around.* The problem in those first moments of freedom was finding something to focus on. On the streets I had my habit to focus on. In jail I'd had my hearings and finally my date to focus on.

I tried to keep my attention on the landscape pounding past me, especially while the train was still in CoCo—Contra Costa—County. Tried to find something familiar in the dips and rounds of the hills and the ash and tar of the streets.

I left without ever going back to the river or walking over the Seventh Street bridge. My feet never touched the concrete or the grass. But I didn't allow myself to think about specifics on that train ride. The minute I thought of home—the minute I thought about leaving behind the people and places that had been the only family I'd known for years—I closed down the past and turned toward the front of the car. I denied myself the memories that would have given meaning to my past and the future looked empty and shapeless.

I am one of those rare individuals for whom one extended stay in the county jail was enough to convince me I never wanted to break another law after half a lifetime of drug addiction and prostitution. Three months gave me enough time to kick and enough straight time to realize that I really didn't want to die young. On the streets and in the middle of it, dying young was just a part of staying alive. But I saw enough hard-timers come and go in those three months to realize that for the most part it was the lucky ones that died young. There were a whole lot of old folks—some who were going to spend the rest of their lives surrounded by razor wire—that went through the county jail while I sat out my time.

Jail was the genesis of my initial desire to move past the needle and the streets and the strange hands on my body. The heavy clanking of doors locking and the enclosed spaces gave rise to the fear that I might not be one of those who died young. Nothing in the past and nothing in the future ever frightened me so much as the thought of a perennial present spent behind locked doors. And the fact that I spent almost two months not knowing if it was going to be three months or three years constantly fueled that fear. I didn't have any violent crime on my sheet, but by that last stay in jail, even I couldn't keep track of how many different charges were pending against me. There were multiple charges, ranging from misdemeanor shoplifting and solicitation to felony burglary, and so many different names attached to them that for the first time in a dozen years, I returned to my birth name in order to keep from confusing myself. And in those first months, the hardest part was leaving identity behind without knowing who I would become.

I'd never been to high school. Never had a real job. Never went through any of the socializing processes that bridge the gap between adolescence and maturity. In jail, when I allowed myself to try to conceive of the future, I tried to imagine what average people my age did with their lives. Jobs and relationships and children and homes. All those things I'd never learned how to do. The only thing that seemed familiar in those first moments of freedom was my name—and even it had been buried and nearly forgotten for almost 15 years.

But my birth name was all I really had left from my childhood and it became my first line of defense in my new world. Hearing it would never remind people of a hooker who spent years doing $20 blow jobs to support a three-bill heroin habit. It was relatively clean and free of damage and I used it like a mask. I reclaimed that name as identity and pretended that the girl who lived so many years of my life with so many different names had never really existed. I adopted the lens through which straight people would have viewed her and I hid her away for what I thought was her own protection.

But you can't just arrive in a small town at the edge of 30 with a 15-year-old hole in your personal history. Friends ask questions and co-workers want to know where you've worked before and what your interests are. They ask if you have kids and you have to have an answer when they want to know why your children don't live with you.

I was a drug addict. It was all I could say for the longest time because it was all I really knew. In the beginning, I made myself a deal. I told the girl I buried inside that once I had half as many years spent in the daylight of the here and now as I spent in the streetlights of her past that I would let her out. I would look at her life. Acknowledge the specifics of memory. I figured on somewhere around seven or eight years it would be safe to remember the names of streets and the color of eyes and the smell of the damp morning grass in June. To think about the red blood and the black heroin. To even begin the process of attaching time to events. The names to the crimes. To cry.

And those five words—*I was a drug addict*—tended to cover everything missing in the narrative of my life and people didn't pry further. I didn't have to name the names or know the dates. They were the words that bought me the first years while I learned how to live this way. While I developed an understanding of the basics. Electricity isn't free. You have to have insurance if you drive. You have to pay for medical care. Walls and a roof to separate the outside from the inside. Sleeping at night and working during the day. Income taxes. Paying for things I got from stores.

But the names and the dates and the specifics of memory came back earlier than I planned. It began with the birth of my daughter in 1991. She tapped into emotions that had dates and names and places and faces attached to them. She stripped away all the calloused layers and exposed the experiences that gave meaning to those emotions. Until I held her, I hadn't realized how much I had prevented myself from feeling by cutting out those 15 years of memory. And I didn't realize until I held her that she had two mothers. She had the woman who'd spent the last few years fishing and running machinery. The woman who'd successfully stayed clean and managed to show up for her life every single day for three years. But she also had the girl who'd run barefoot through the streets for half her life. The girl who learned about truth and guts and commitment from prostitutes and gangsters and junkies. They were of course the same person, but I had so distinctly segregated them that I didn't initially understand that she not only belonged to both of us—she needed both of us.

And so the memories returned—specific and in detail. But they were still the experiences of a different person. Me but not me. I could create pictures of the moments, but I was never in them. She was never in them. I couldn't find the woman I was now or the girl I had been anywhere on that landscape. And every once in a while I would wonder if it had really happened. Asked myself if I was entirely sure that I knew where I'd spent those 15 years.

And I became afraid that if I waited the whole seven or eight years to open all the doors, there wouldn't be anything or anybody left, that there would be no one left to confirm my memories, and so the search became something of a race. I contacted various police departments where I could remember having been booked for one crime or another, hoping to be allowed to look at records or mug shots, but they all told me that the general public couldn't have access to those records. After that I thought about the newspaper. We didn't have much access to media back in the day—but we had from time to time made use of the newspaper. The Contra Costa Times always had a police blotter-type column and we'd sometimes used it to keep track of who was in and who was out of the joint. Who died and sometimes even who did it. But even with names and approximate dates, the paper couldn't help. They didn't have time and I hadn't yet figured out how to narrow down the parameters of my search.

Finally I decided the best chance I had of finding anything was to find my old man. Darryl Masters was about as much of an institution as anyone ever got to be in that life—mostly because of his age and how much time he'd done. He had experience and the smarts to put it to good use and if anybody was still alive, I figured it would be him. Furthermore he'd been in and out of institutions since the age of 10 and I knew if he was alive the state of California would be tracking him—at least to the best of their ability. It took less than three phone calls and a half-hour to find him.

In the first letter I wrote him, I was so unsure of my own recall that I prefaced the letter with *You may not remember me—but …* When we finally hooked up on the phone the first time, he laughed about that. "'You may not remember me?' What's that all about, Girl? How I'm gonna forget ya? Don't just forget years of your life like that do ya?" And once we started writing—once I had his letters to touch and read—I recognized his handwriting. There was finally some tangible evidence that I/she (or we) had existed. He called me by her name. The first letter I got from him was addressed to me—Megan Foss. But inside he wrote *Dear Mickey.*

He did seven months that time and we'd talked often about him coming to visit me, but he was like all old-time junkies. He'd make parole and be fixing dope within hours and then he couldn't go test for his parole officer and the run was on. I heard from him once in the next year and a half and then in April of '95, he got busted again and started calling and writing.

In June I finally went back. Darryl had told me what had become of almost everybody I could remember and by then there almost wasn't anybody left. Most all the girls I'd worked the night shift with were gone. There were a few old-timers like Darryl left—but for the most part, it seemed like everybody had lost their life or was doing life. And Darryl was locked up when I had the window of time and opportunity that allowed me to go back, so in the end I went in search of my past with no one from it to help make sense of it—except of course for Mickey.

II

CoCo in June is usually hot and already withered and dry. But June was uncommonly wet and the rain pounding on the black tar and concrete steamed and smelled like an odd combination of hot metal and cut grass. One moment the sign that announced my entry was ahead of me and one moment later it was behind me, but even without the sign, I would have known exactly when I crossed the county line. Would have known the land and ground and water and sky that had been home for so many years the same way I recognized my mother after our extended separation. It was hard-wired into me.

I didn't quite realize it until making that crossing, but I loved and missed the land at least as much as the people. I'd run wild through those streets and like some children long for the homes they grew up in, Mickey had spent the last eight years longing to feel the dust rising up around her bare feet or the crunch of gravel beneath spike heels. The feeling of the river grass pressed against her cheeks at night. For years I'd walked with her just barely an inch outside me—always a shadowed outline—and as I pulled onto Highway 4 and saw the valley spread out before me with the lights of Bella Vista dappled across the delta I wondered if she would finally move into sync.

Bella Vista is east. East of San Francisco. East of Concord and Pleasant Hill. East of the valley and east of the interstate. East of civilization. Virtually east of everything and when I lived on its streets it was incredibly isolated. The Bart train didn't hook up to the city back then and only a few brave souls were willing to battle the god-awful traffic and commute the 40 or so miles into San Francisco. But that had changed.

I went straight out Highway 4 and from a distance coming over the hill, it looked much the same. Flat and low with the old steel mill providing the tallest point of reference and the river in the distance. And when I got off at the West Pittsburg off-ramp, the same liquor store still stood on the corner on the right. Willow Pass Road still ran the main length of what I remembered as a run-down, poverty-stricken town deconstructing around itself, but little else looked familiar.

I drove south as far as Bailey Road and got caught at the light. I could see all the way up to the freeway on-ramp, but there was a series of parking lots and small businesses where there used to just be the two-lane road that wound its way over the hill—the road that I hitchhiked a hundred times moving between the cranksters on the west side and the junkies on the east. I'd come over that hill almost 15 years before and made Bella Vista my home after traveling and running and calling nowhere home since I'd left my mother's house for the first time at the age of 14.

The next few blocks had been the stroll. The working girls had been pretty much free to walk between Bailey at the one end and Balcutha at the other. And the first few blocks looked the same. The small narrow park on the left and two small restaurants before you got to the cantina where we'd done our best business. But where we'd walked in the dust and the gravel, they'd put in sidewalks. Formed squares of cement instead of the uneven bumpy shoulder.

There were still the two bars right in a row. The cantina and what had been Marg's country-western bar next door. Only now I couldn't tell if it was country. There weren't any cowboys hanging in front or in the parking lot negotiating date prices with girls in cut-offs and spike heels. And there weren't any girls.

It seemed like there were dozens of small businesses. Especially the closer you got to Bailey Road. I noticed an insurance office and two real estate brokers as well as a hardware store and a bank. I couldn't remember there ever having been a bank in Bella Vista. If there'd been a bank in Bella Vista back in the day, it would have got hit every other week. You could have banks in Martinez or Pleasant Hill or Concord. Cranksters are too paranoid to do anything as organized as a bank. Junkies will hit anything if they get sick enough.

I wouldn't have expected to see much traffic at that time of night. Just sheriffs and the occasional john. Maybe a tweak on their way to cop in cars that had long ago had their tape decks ripped out. And I didn't see much traffic, but the cars I did see looked like they were being driven by normal people. Maybe somebody going out for a quart of milk for breakfast in the morning or somebody just getting home from a second shift at some tech job over the hill. The cars all looked interchangeable. Sturdy. Economical. Functional. And none of them looked as if they doubled as homes. I chuckled when I realized that my four-door Geo Metro blended right in.

When I crossed Bailey I squinted up at the Taco Bell windows. The Taco Bell had been one of the few places they'd let us go in. At least they'd let us in if we had shoes and money. The only other places that we could go in were the liquor stores and the cantina. The two restaurants and Marg's wouldn't let us step foot across the doorsill because they didn't want us bothering the customers. Wasn't much danger of that happening at Taco Bell and sometimes we'd go in and buy sodas and then borrow the key to the bathroom and go in there to shoot our dope.

I drove a little farther and then pulled into the laundromat at the corner of Broadway. The sign still said "Open 24 hours a day." The Pepsi machine still hummed from the neon glowing red white and blue onto the otherwise colorless night. But there was a sign on the wall beside the Pepsi machine that said something about only those people using the machines being allowed to use the premises and I wondered where the street people went to get out of the cold at night nowadays.

I could see "The Tonight Show" on a TV in the corner that had never been there before. Even chained down, the TV wouldn't have lasted a week. Everybody with a car had bolt-cutters. Bolt-cutters were standard issue along with black tape and Krazy Glue. Everything we needed to take the world apart and put it back together.

And then I caught myself thinking that I needed to move before people noticed me watching. But none of these people looked like the kind of people that got nervous if they happened to catch someone scoping them. These people were busy doing what they'd gone there to do and if they noticed me at all they didn't strain their brains trying to figure out if I was going to take their dope or turn out to be a fed. Sitting there with the bright lights and the evidence of such blatant normalcy in every direction I thought for a minute that I must have lived through those years in some kind of alternate reality. Like on a "Star Trek" episode where something gets disrupted on the time-line and the future doesn't turn out the way it was meant to. And I kept waiting for Mickey to say something. To point and say there—I remember that. But she stayed quiet. Shocked—I think as much by those things that were the same as by those things that felt utterly alien. As much hurt by what had happened to her home as she was nourished by what little remained.

After three days I was starting to be sorry I'd come. Never seeing any of it again would have been better than looking and not being sure it was ever there in the first place.

I thought about all the times Darryl had told me how much had changed. *I feel so sorry for them girls. Most all them girls got AIDS now. Without the girls there ain't no way to maintain the heroin economy. Them people are all fuckin' pitiful. I seen Randy Hinton collecting aluminum cans the last time I drove down Willow Pass Road. All them girls got AIDS now. I tell ya, Mickey—Pittsburg's dead. I don't never even go into Bella Vista except to deliver.*

Heroin dried up with the girls and Darryl said that left a hole in the market that crack was custom-made to fill. *But the youngsters these days are fuckin' crazy, Mickey. They all packing major fuckin' artillery and they shoot at anything. They got no honor. How old were we when we were out there, Girl? We wasn't no kids. It's scandalous shit goin' on. Whole neighborhood's gone to shit.*

No girls and a bunch of boys packing guns. Back in the day, it had been the girls that held the weapons. We needed them for protection, but we never pulled them except to save our money or our lives. The guys didn't pack because it always tacked on an extra 90 days when they got popped for parole violations. And mostly they didn't need them. Mostly we didn't kill each other.

Darryl told me that everybody was gone—that nobody worked or lived on the streets—and I'd accepted that idea long before I ever went back. I hadn't expected to go there and find the same people in the same places. But what surprised me most was the feeling that they'd all been hounded to their deaths or rounded up and put behind razor-wire somewhere. That there'd been a bloodless coup. I had expected to find everybody gone because that's what Darryl told me and because my own experience of the streets was that virtually nobody could survive and stay free for all the years that I'd been somewhere else. But it wasn't like it had happened naturally. It was like a campaign had been waged and it hadn't even been much of a battle. Restrict access to fresh water. Build homes so close together you can't even grow a rosebush in the ground that separates them. Sweep the stroll so often the johns won't come out because they don't want their names to end up in the paper. Starve them out.

That would have had to have been accomplished before they got developers to go in there and build all those houses for all those families. They would have had to invest some serious time to get those streets safe enough for family living. From the freeway you could get an overall picture of the changes. You could see the lack of free space. The crowded houses built right up to the river and the two-lane streets that had been widened to four lanes and the neon signs that heralded a different kind of economy than had governed in the past. It all looked like a model for a larger city's get-tough-on-crime policy. And in theory that's all a good thing. That's what the earth is for. To grow healthy, functional families in healthy, functional communities. But it didn't feel good. It felt like a new generation of people had built its happiness and its future on the bones and memories of my past. And worse than that, it felt like it had happened without any acknowledgment of the lives it must have cost.

I wondered how many city council meetings it had taken. How many tax levies. It didn't look like they'd required any additional personnel. In almost a week I'd seen just the two cops. I never would have thought it possible that I could miss the presence of CoCo's finest, but their absence was a critical indicator in the whole biosphere. On the one hand, it all seemed like a classic example of an environment becoming hostile to its native tribe and on the other, it seemed like a textbook case of successful reclamation.

And as I passed Bailey and headed out across the valley, I couldn't avoid wondering what had happened to all the people who'd lived on that land they'd spent so much money reclaiming. There'd been at least 20 working girls and the money they earned supported at least 40 habits. And they'd slept in the spaces that were no longer empty and worked on the streets that no longer had places to conduct business and they'd communicated their needs over phone lines no longer intact. Washed their hair and their bodies in water they no longer had access to. Not even counting all the lives beyond those 40 people that depended in one way or another on that community and that economy being there—that still left the 40 and I wondered if anybody in any of those city council meetings or those board rooms had ever given a thought to the indigenous population. I'd expected to find them all gone, but I hadn't expected something else to be in their place.

Dawn was still there. She lived with Preacher Bob in a trailer right off Willow Pass on Broadway. Back behind the migrant shacks we'd called the Del Monte. And they had a phone there. I knew that because Darryl had given me the number. Guys that do time on a regular basis always know who's got a phone and after all the years that had passed, when Darryl got busted, he still called me and he still called Dawn.

But I didn't call before I went over the last Saturday night I was there. I waited until I figured most of her traffic would have died down and drove back to Bella Vista to see her. Darryl never got real specific about what she was up to. When I asked, he always said, "Same old shit." And I'd always say, "Damn."

She'd belonged to Darryl a long time ago. She was the girl before me, which meant that if she was still doing the same old shit, she'd been doing it for close on 20 years now. She was an old-timer when I was new. I didn't think she was actually any older than me, but she'd been there since she was 14. Darryl said that she was still with Carlos but that he was doing 10 to 20 at Pelican Bay.

Dawn got herself off the stroll and pretty much set for life when she hooked up with Carlos. Carlos came into town with a huge bag of dope and unlimited access to more. He didn't speak much English in the beginning but somehow Dawn managed to understand everything he said. And she spoke English but slurred and ran her words so bad that even those of us who spent months and years with her had a hard time understanding her. But Carlos could. He was the perfect example of the dealer who came to town and fell for the hooker as hard as the hooker fell for the habit. He never got rich or wore thick gold chains, but he kept her fixed and both of them supplied with rocks for years on end and from what Darryl said, she was managing to keep the business alive in his absence.

Heroin dealers most always quit dealing by 7 in the evening. Sometimes earlier in the winter. And I figured she would have been done and closed up for the night by the time I pulled down Broadway looking for her trailer. I had the address, but even if I hadn't, I could have picked the place out. Used to be a tweak or a dealer living in every other trailer and it was hard to tell one from the other, but now most of them had flowers and gates and porches with lawn chairs like people actually came out in the light of day.

Except for number 766. Dawn's place didn't betray a sign of life.

Not a flower living in a pot. Not a blade of grass growing amongst the dirt and gravel that were its yard. Not even a porch light, but even in the dark you could see that the last 6 in the black house numbers was hanging upside down.

The other places had cars with infant seats and four doors—and some of the lots even had neatly appointed storage sheds. But the screen on Dawn's door hung on one hinge and had a huge tear in the bottom half panel and I wondered how she'd managed to hold out in the face of such an obvious attempt to eradicate her kind.

I thought I saw blinds blink when I turned my lights off and killed the motor. I looked down at my legs. At my feet. At the clothes I was wearing. I lifted my hand to touch the earrings I'd put on. She wouldn't know me. I wouldn't have known me. If I'd been her and saw my car pull up I would have had someone posted right close to the toilet and ready to flush. She used to have nightmares about not being able to flush her toilet. I could remember sleeping beside her on the living room floor under a sleeping bag and waking up with her fingers digging into my shoulder. *I can't flush the toilet.*

She got worse after Carlos went away the first time. He'd spoiled her. He kept dope in her spoon and rock in her pipe and she never had to think about anything. Dawn was always the only junkie I knew whose life was so easy she could afford to get high. The rest of us struggled so hard just to stay ahead of our sick that we never really tasted that. But she never had to leave her spoon. She just sat there and waited for the dope to fill it up. Carlos made it all easy for Dawn—until he went away.

Then she had to deal with customers and cash and scales and details. She never quite came out of the nod she went into during those early years with Carlos and it initially surprised me when Darryl told me she was still there and still with Carlos and still throwing. That meant she'd made it to damn near 40 without drawing serious time—amazing. But after I thought about it, it made sense. Of us all—Dawn was the most a homegirl. She knew the alleys and the back ways and the tunnels and the attics and the cellars of Bella Vista better than any city planner looking at blueprints could have ever known them. It would have been like the Warsaw Ghetto Battle trying to get her out of there. She would have tossed bottle rockets if that's all she had and she never would have gone down alive.

Somebody in the trailer across the street opened their front door and looked at my car. I could remember times when I would have given anything to look as normal I did now. To be able to move through crowds in malls without having security guards step in behind me. To be able to walk in a bar without getting asked to leave. But being normal made me look strange now because people like me didn't visit people like Dawn.

I searched my mind and couldn't find a single memory of sitting in a place like Dawn's and having someone normal like me show up at the door. People looking to cop came to the door and hookers with dates came to the door and sometimes somebody with a bullet in a shoulder or a limb gouged or partially severed from a knife wound came to the door. Ambulance attendants came to the door. The sheriffs sometimes came to the door and sometimes it even got as particular as somebody's parole officer coming to the door. But nobody driving a '95 electric-green Geo who just stopped by to catch up on old times ever came to the door.

Sitting in my car and then standing on the step and pulling away the screen door, I'd forgotten that Darryl said she was living with Preacher Bob. I had no idea who Preacher Bob was, but Darryl said he was some old guy with glasses who ran check scams and that I definitely knew him. He even said we'd stayed with him once in some apartment at Shore Acres, but I hadn't been able to think of anybody who'd been known as Preacher anything. And so he slipped my mind until the door opened and he stood there with the fabric of a tank-style T-shirt stretched across his bulging gut in a pair of dirty brown slacks with thin black suspenders dangling at his sides. Two-thirds bald, but the hair that still grew was thick and wavy and white on his shoulders and his chin. Santa with a habit.

He took up most of the doorway and just stared at me. Something about him did look familiar, but I couldn't figure out why or where.

He was obviously going to wait until I said something, so I did. "Is Dawn here?"

He leaned into the door frame and ran his forearm under his nose, but he didn't answer me.

"Is Dawn around?" I asked again and tried to see behind him, but the only light in the place came from somewhere in the back and I couldn't see anything but vague outlines.

He still didn't answer and I started to feel uncomfortable. It bothered me that I could feel so alien in exactly the kind of place I thought of as back home during the years I'd been away. And I was starting to feel a little desperate. I was going to try invoking Darryl's name and see if that lightened the mood at all. "I was told Dawn was living here. I'm a friend of—" But he didn't let me finish.

"I know who ya are," he said and stepped back a couple steps. He didn't say it hostile, but he didn't say it warm either.

"How do you know me?" I asked.

"I remember."

"What do you remember?"

"I remember everybody come through this place. I'm old. I ain't senile."

"Darryl said I knew you, but I can't remember."

"It was a while ago."

"Yeah—I guess," I said and turned to look at the room. Inside it looked even darker. There was a kitchen on the left with dishes scattered everywhere and something snapping and popping in a skillet full of grease on the stove. They had a flimsy plastic-and-aluminum dinette set and my eyes went to the half-full glass of water and the torn cigarette filter lying beside the bottlecap with the wire twisted around it. The wire that kept fingers from getting burned when a flame was held under the cap.

He pointed toward the light in the back and said, "She's in her room. I'll get her."

He walked across the living room and hollered. "Hey. Ya got company." He waited for a couple seconds and then yelled again. "Ya hear me, Girl? Get up." And I heard her mumble something in the background. Barely intelligible. But in a familiar way. She'd always spoken gibberish. Only every third or fourth word had ever made sense.

"Come see for yourself," he yelled at her and then I saw her shadow on the wall moving forward and away from the light. He had to move so she could pass by him in the narrow entryway and there in the half-light, she looked so much the same. She was tall—at least two inches taller than my 5-foot-7 frame—but smaller in every other way. None of us had much fat on us, but most of the girls developed pretty decent muscles walking the streets. Dawn didn't have muscle or fat. By the end of the last winter I went through with her, she looked like flesh shrink-wrapped around bones. And in the shadow she still looked that way. But when she came close enough so that I could make out her features and take in the details of her appearance, the first thing I noticed was that the skin hadn't stayed tight. The curse of skinny women. They start to age and there's no fat or tissue to hold the skin up. Gravity. Her cheeks sagged like they were suspended from the high sharp bones in her face and I couldn't decide whether I would have known her or not if I'd seen her outside her environment.

Her face was still shaped like a heart and the eyes still tipped in that way that she thought made her look exotic. She painted huge lines on her eyes and carried the line out and up at the corners to accent their natural shape. The hair was still long—maybe as long—but it had thinned and faded and I couldn't even quite make out the shade. It had too much color to be gray but not enough to be anything else and it seemed to have lost most of its weight. It fell away from her face and then feathered down around her shoulders and hips in wisps and strands.

"Hey," I said and smiled as I stepped forward. If it hadn't been for the old man knowing me from somewhere, I would have known what to say. I would have said *You probably don't remember me, but I used to work out here—10 and 15 years ago.* But the fact that he knew me and I still couldn't place him made that feel awkward.

Dawn dragged her hand across her forehead to wipe stray hairs away and then held it over her eyes like a visor. She wobbled and reached out into the air to steady herself with her other arm.

"Yeah?" she said. I looked to the old man to see if he was going to take the lead, but he just stood there staring and scratching his chest.

I turned back to her. "I don't suppose you remember me?"

The eyes narrowed further until I couldn't even see the irises. She shook her head slightly. "No. Who are ya?"

If I hadn't been looking right at her, I wouldn't have been able to make out her words. I didn't say anything and she turned and walked over to twist the switch on the floor lamp with the bare bulb.

"Who are ya?" She'd wrapped her arms tight around her waist and was starting to look spooked. It was good that the old man had somehow recognized me. I never would have got through the front door otherwise. The fact that he let me in and told her to come out was the only thing keeping her from bolting and I'd bet money she had at least a half-dozen escape routes in that place. I never would have been able to find her.

"Megan. Remember? I was with Darryl. We—you and I—we ran together for a couple years here."

Her eyes widened just a titch and then she shook her head and moved toward the dinette. "I don't think I know ya. Whaddaya want?"

That question was easy. "I don't live here anymore. I been gone for a long time and I wanted to come back to see if it was the same."

"Ya were with Darryl?" she said and slipped into a chair. "Darryl calls me. He called a week or so ago." Then she turned to the old man. "It was a week or so ago, wasn't it? Didn't Darryl call a week or so back?"

"Yup," he said and drew on his cigarette. "Calls every week. Never sends money for the phone bill, but he calls most every week."

"I knew he called," she said and dropped her head on her chest. And then just as suddenly it bobbed back up. "Where is he?" she asked and looked from me to the old man.

I answered her. "He's at Quentin. He's doing a violation."

"How do ya know that?"

"'Cause he calls me too. That's how I had your address. He gave it to me."

"Why would he give ya my address?"

"'Cause he knew I was coming down here and wanted to see you. Do you remember back when Carlos first came to town? Darryl said you're still with Carlos. I was here when you first met Carlos. Remember?"

Her head dropped again. "Carlos's gone," I thought she said. And then she looked up again. "Whaddaya want? I don't got nothin'." I didn't answer right away and she called on the old man. "Tell her. I don't got nothin' do I?"

He didn't respond.

"I don't want anything, Dawn. I just wanted to see you. To know how you were. I thought about you a bunch of times over the years and I just wanted to see you."

I started to move toward the door. I wanted to leave. I hadn't intended to upset her. It hadn't occurred to me that I wouldn't be able to convince her that she knew me. I'd wondered how long it would take her to recognize me but not whether or not she ever would.

"You're a friend of Darryl's?" she asked and I stopped.

"Yeah. Yours too." She put some spit on her fingers and rubbed at the blood that had started to dry on the back of her arm. She said something and I couldn't understand her at all because she had her head down and the hair fell across her face.

"What?" I asked.

She brushed the hair away and got her eyelids most of the way up. She looked like she was trying to focus and then she started to say something but stopped with her mouth hanging wide open. She put her hand on my arm and it looked like the turkey claws the neighborhood dogs dragged home from the turkey farm around Thanksgiving time. Scaly with red blotches and fingers that permanently curved into hooks. Then she moved the fingers up and rested them against my cheek—fingers fanned out across my face as if she were trying to read it through her fingertips.

"Mickey," she whispered.

Tiny bumps raised all over my flesh and I felt my eyes smart with tears. I nodded my head with her fingers still on my cheek. "Yeah— Mickey," I said back to her and she smiled. And when she smiled, the years dropped away. Darryl called me Mickey but it was across phone lines strung over a thousand miles. It helped me believe in my past, but it still wasn't solid. He couldn't see the face attached to the voice and the name. Couldn't be entirely sure I was the same person. But Dawn, finally—after all the years—put the name with the face.

"Ya look so differnt," she said.

"I got my teeth fixed."

"There's more."

"I got old," I said and laughed.

She took her hand from my cheek and tossed her head back and hair flew everywhere. "Ain't we all."

I nodded. "Yeah." I couldn't come up with more words. I had too many things rushing through the mind. Mickey and Megan. Megan and Mickey. The same. She knew me. We had the same memories.

"I think Darryl told me ya were comin'," she said.

"Yeah?"

"Yeah. He talks about ya a lot. Said ya go to some fancy college somewhere by Canada."

"Washington. It's in Washington and it's not fancy at all."

"So what are ya doin' here?"

"I came to see you."

Her head lolled on her left shoulder and her eyes kept rolling back. Then suddenly she came to attention and said something so fast I lost her after the first couple words.

I leaned toward her. "I didn't hear you."

"I said ya can fix me. I been tryin' to get a hit for two days."

The old man stepped over to the table and put his hand on her shoulder. "Skin-pop it, Girl. Ya gonna end up killin' yourself."

She shrugged his touch away. "Noo. She can fix me. I remember."

She shoved her arm out at me and slapped at her veins. "I remember. Ya can do it." You could still see her veins beneath the skin that looked like onion paper. There were holes and ruptures all along them, but you could still see the blue beds. Her problem had never been finding a vein. Her problem had always been holding one. She had rollers. Great huge rollers that looked like they should have been so easy to spike, but the minute she got flash in her syringe and started to fire, the vein would move and she'd dump her dope in the muscle where it had been.

In the weeks right after Darryl went away that first time I'd stayed with Dawn and Carlos and one of the reasons she'd taken me in without asking for anything in return was because I could fix her. I could hit the veins in the soft underside of her arm near the pit. I could hit her neck. And I could even hit the small feather veins in her ankles if she held still enough.

She'd get up in the morning and cook up close to a half-gram of stuff and as long as I could fix her, I got half. I shook my head. "No. I don't wanna try to fix you."

"I didn't ask if ya wanted to. I asked if ya could." She smiled when she said it.

I heard the old man chuckle and then he looked right in my eyes. "Ya can do it."

Dawn started digging in the pocket of her jeans and then dropped a ball that looked like at least a solid gram on the table and started to unwrap the foil and after that the plastic wrap from the shiny brown dope.

I pushed my chair back and started to get up, but she grabbed at my arm. "Don't go."

"Dawn, I don't wanna do this. It's been years since I fixed anybody."

"It's like ridin' a bike," the old man said. "Ya never forget."

I turned from Dawn to the old man. "Who the fuck are you?"

Dawn didn't let him answer. She told him to get her rig and the next thing I knew her kit bag was on the table and she was stripping the paper away from a 100-unit syringe.

"Dawn, I'm not gonna fix you," I said, but it didn't slow her down at all. She grabbed the bottlecap and used her finger to dig out the used cotton ball and then she used the tail of her shirt to wipe it clean. She moved too fast reaching for the water and almost fell off her chair. I put my hand out to steady her, but she pushed it away.

"Yeah, ya will," was all she said before pulling a tiny knife out from another pocket. She cut the piece of dope in half and then took one of the halves and cut it into smaller sections and dropped them off the blade of the knife into the bottlecap. She went to put the syringe into the glass to draw water, but she wobbled again and jammed the needle into the bottom of the glass.

"Shit," she muttered and pulled it out to inspect the damage. It wasn't bent and didn't appear to have any visible barbs, but it was hard to tell.

"Let me see it," I said and held my hand out. I gently dragged the needle across my bare arm to see if I could feel any spurs or if it scratched, but it felt smooth and clean.

"Gimme the water," I told her and she slid it across to me. I drew up almost 50 units of water and she started shaking her head.

"Noo—too much water."

I'd forgotten. She only used enough water to cook. Less water meant a stronger shot. And less fluid in the barrel left more room to move once you got blood in it. If you missed and went to go again, you didn't want the rig full—you still needed room to draw back. I squirted half the water back in the glass and the rest over the dope in the bottlecap. They'd been using matches—there were matchsticks all over the table burned down so low fingers must have got hot. I got my lighter out and holding the cap in one hand and my lighter in the other, I started to cook.

I let it go until it bubbled and the thick rich fumes filled the room. When I was a kid we shot the China White and everybody seemed to agree that it was better dope than the tar the Mexicans brought over the border, but I loved the way the tar smelled. Bitter like black coffee but sweet like caramel all at the same time.

While I cooked she tore a piece of cotton from the cigarette filter and rolled it into a ball. I set the cap down and used the top of the plunger to stir and make sure it had all cooked and mixed. She dropped the cotton ball in it and stared at me—sitting there with the syringe in my hand and the dope in front of me.

"Dawn, I'm not gonna fix you with that much dope."

"I do that much all the time. It's safe."

"I'm not doing it."

Then the old man piped up. "I seen her do more dope than that when she wasn't sick. Hell—I seen you do more dope than that."

"Who are you?" I asked.

"Never mind," Dawn said and pointed at the dope. "Do it."

"Dawn, I don't care how safe you say it is. They got laws about people who fix other people and then those people die. You can go to prison for that shit."

Her voice went way up. "I ain't gonna die. And if I did, I wouldn't tell anybody ya did it." There was silence for a couple seconds while we held one another's eyes. "Come on," she smiled when she said it. "Ya done me with more dope than that before. Nothing's changed."

I thought for a second about all the things that had changed. The things that had changed and the things that had stayed the same. I could remember a thousand times I'd sat for hours poking holes in my veins—desperate to get a vein. The panic and the frustration.

"I got a kid now, Dawn. I'll help you, but I'm not gonna hit you with all that dope. I'm sure you could do that much and then some— but I got a kid now and I'm not taking that chance."

When I said it I hadn't expected it to make any difference to her begging—but I'd forgotten what children meant. You could do almost anything and if you were doing it for the sake of a child, nobody in that life would ever question it. Children were sacred. Probably because there weren't any and she mellowed after I said that.

"OK," she said, "but make it a good one."

I nodded and gently pressed the tip of the needle on the cotton ball and slowly pulled back on the plunger—watching the thick dark antidote fill up the barrel. It took three draws, but I got everything up in it. On the last draw I flipped it over and pushed the plunger until one tiny drop of dope came through the eye of the needle. I got a little over 50 units altogether and I squirted close to half of it back in the cap and then held the rig up for her inspection.

"OK?"

"Yeah I guess," she said. And then, "Where ya wanna try it?"

"Where's the last place you got a clean hit?"

She screwed up her face for a second and then said, "I think behind my knees."

I looked around to see if there was another light we could turn on and didn't see any. "How long since you tried under your arm? Up high," I said and lifted her arm up over her head. The entire Union Pacific could have run on those tracks. Thick calloused maps of welts vividly etched on skin the color of skim milk. But the veins were still there.

"Lay down on the floor," I told her and without a word she lay on her back on the kitchen floor.

I knelt down on the left beside her and the old man came and stood over me. "What the Hell are ya doin' on the floor?" he demanded.

I turned to him. "I guess you don't remember everything—and you're in my light." I returned my attention to Dawn and the shadow passed out of what little light there was. The trick with hitting Dawn had always been getting her to be still. I'd discovered a long time ago that if I got her to lie flat on the floor with her arm over her head, she didn't move. I got her solid on the first try.

I watched her for a couple seconds. I knew a quarter-gram of stuff wouldn't be anywhere near enough to take her over the edge, but I watched anyway, just to make sure. After a couple seconds she ran her tongue over her lips and I knew she was tasting it—on her tongue. On her lips. Her eyes finally closed all the way and she just lay there and enjoyed that which she got so rarely—a clean hit.

I got up and moved to the table to clean the rig. As soon as he saw it was a clean shot, the old man said, "Damn," and moved in on the remains in the bottlecap.

I filled the barrel full of water and squirted it at the wadded-up towel on the floor that they'd obviously been using for just that purpose. It had hundreds of tiny blood spots on it and I added a new arc.

When it was clean I put the orange cap back over the needle. "Does she save these?"

He was just about to hit himself. "Yeah—she'll use it a couple times."

She'd started to move—had pulled herself up to a sitting position and was softly rubbing her hands over her bare arms. I moved toward her.

"Dawn?"

No answer. I put my hand on her shoulder and shook it just a tiny bit. "Dawn?"

"She can't hear ya," came from the old man. I knew that. I knew Dawn. She nodded like no junkie I'd ever seen and she wouldn't be making any kind of sense for at least a couple hours.

I grabbed my jacket off the back of the chair I'd hung it on. The old man had got his hit by then, but he didn't nod off like she did. His eyes drooped just a little, but he was still with me.

"If you get her to lay down where she's not moving, you can fix her. Her underarms will hold out for a while and you can get her neck the same way."

"You're a good girl, Mickey."

I stared at him. Trying to figure out why the voice sounded familiar. What it was I recognized.

And then he repeated himself. "You're a good girl."

"Do me a favor," I asked and he nodded before I told him what it was. "Tell her I was here."

"I'll tell her, but she won't remember."

I turned the doorknob and looked back one last time. "Who are you?"

"Preacher Bob. It'll come to ya."

III

What I saw in Bella Vista infected my dreams for a long time. I'd dream that it was nine years ago and I was walking down Broadway in my cut-offs and tank top to meet a dealer and then just when he was, going to drop the dope in my hand—everything would shift from the way it had been to the way it is now. And instead of a dealer I'd find myself staring at Preacher Bob and when I asked him where I was he'd just say, "It'll come to ya."

I knew that with AIDS and all that, it would have changed. I knew that for the most part junkies just don't get old. But it all looked like it had been part of a plan. Like they decided to give Bella Vista a face lift and all the people and places that were my family and my home were old and excess skin.

And it was wrong. That land had been ours. We never held title to it—but after all those years we should have had homestead rights. We had been a culture—a society—and now we were within a generation of becoming extinct. Nothing left but an old man and a rag-tag junkie who'd been so isolated by the modernization that she'd almost lost her ability to communicate.

There should have been another way. We talk about reclaiming our streets like it's some kind of honorable mission—but we do it without any consideration for the people. We do that because we don't think of them as people. We reduce them to nothing more than the chemicals they ingest or the tricks they turn. They're junkies or prostitutes, but they're never someone's mother or someone's child. They're statistics on the evening news and the enemy in the war on crime.

But I knew them—I remember the specifics of their lives. They were like me and I was like them and here I am and so they could have been too. I frequently get told—when people find out about my past—that I'm the exception to the rule. I understand that it's intended as a compliment, but it bothers me. I'm not the exception to any rule. The only difference between me and Dawn was that I had someone to give me a chance. But it comforts people to believe that such lives are irretrievably lost. That alleviates any feelings of responsibility or guilt.

But they need to feel responsible and they need to feel guilt. When they lie down in their beds at night in houses that have their foundations lodged in the land that was our home—they need to remember that their great American dream was somebody else's great American tragedy. And they need to understand their complicity. Every girl on that street represented a societal failure. Every girl on that street was somebody that nobody else cared about. And no one wants to acknowledge the humanity of such people when they see them, much less remember them when they're gone.

But I remember. That's what I went back there to do. To find my memories. And I did. The only person I found who could confirm my existence was an old man that I couldn't recall ever knowing and a junkie who could barely remember who she was. But there had been those moments—her hand on my cheek. The red flash in the syringe when I hit her vein. Only Mickey could have recognized those moments.

Megan Foss *earned her M.A. at Western Washington University and now lives in Pittsburgh, where she teaches at the Allegheny County Jail. Additionally, she teaches at the University of Pittsburgh, where she is completing her M.F.A. in creative nonfiction. Foss is the recipient of the 1998 Rona Jaffe Award.*

Cover to Cover

Reviews of New Books

Prozac Diary
by Lauren Slater

One pill makes you larger and one pill makes you small. And the ones that mother gives you, don't do anything at all —Jefferson Airplane

At the end of the first chapter of "Prozac Diary," Lauren Slater sits on a stool in her kitchen. I like to imagine it is the same stool on which she sits for the photograph on the book jacket. I like to imagine that the look on her face is also the same. It is 1988 and the moment when she contemplates being one of the first patients to take a small green and beige pill just prescribed by the "Prozac Doctor." It is an earthy look, a bit tense, interested but not forward, intelligent but not arrogant. It plays with the camera, the outside world, but is solidly inward. I imagine it is this look from where she writes.

I too sit on a stool in my kitchen. I'm fingering the book jacket that mirrors the exact same green and beige hues of the pill she is about to take. You might assume that this pill and the book I hold

Random House, 1998, 203 pp

have little in common besides these outward marketing maneuvers, but you would be wrong. This book is just as surely a capsule that transports the reader on as difficult a journey as the one Slater holds in her fingertips.

Slater arranges the book in eight chapters that move the story forward in one voice. From the first prescription, the first ingestion, the subsequent behavioral changes related to the drug, the role of Benjamin, the man with whom she falls in love and marries, to the drug's failure and finding of her own will, the story takes place in the unsettled, subjective, recent past. She struggles with the girl whose identity, wrested from the easy rocking and lulling familiarity of her illness, is chemically tossed into the stormy brine of the unknown state of "health." The process raises fundamental questions. Who was I then? If that was the real me then, am I real now? If I am real now, why do I long so for the missing old me? And what is health anyway?

This is the voice of the sensual Slater, the "fine boned, indigo-veined girl" for whom the air can feel like "flannel on her skin." This is the voice of a young woman with a personal sun whose rays "rustle like a silk dress." This is the humorous metaphorian, who, when the drug once fails her, a problem known in the field as "Prozac poop-out," describes it as a "drug with a prostate problem, a drug with sexual dysfunction, a goddamn impotent little Prozac penis." This is the voice of the post-modern Slater, raising fundamental questions to which psychoanalytic, philosophical and neurophysiological tomes have devoted themselves. Is there one true core self or are we multiple selves? Is the proposition of a core self a necessary illusion created by the brain's propensity for a modular and hierarchically arranged organizing system and minimal expenditure of energy? Are we simply a pool of chemicals and system of synapses whose idiosyncratic looping and bending can be easily altered by adding a little green here and a little beige there?

To this voice, Slater adds two more in six smaller essays called "Letters to my Doctor." Each of these letters begins with one or two questions from an eventual total of eight that read like a questionnaire typical of those required for a hospitalization—the voice of the cool, clinical, Cartesian professional collecting the objective facts about the patient's current functioning, family history, symptomotology and diagnosis.

These portions are staccato segments separated from the responses and the main text by font and tone. They more graphically raise other questions alluded to throughout the book, including the book's critical focus—the relationship of the doctor to the patient's difficulties and the issue of personal identity. When she raises the question of whether Prozac is a wonder drug or one that triggers violence, she responds with a lesson for all clinicians. "For me Prozac lies not between these poles but entirely outside them in a place my doctor was not taught to go— the difficulty and compromise of cure, the grief and light of illness passing. Cure is a complex, disorienting, a revisioning of self," she writes to remind healers "to smooth the skin."

In poignant and softer italics, but glaring juxtaposition, she answers the questionnaire with the more tender, humane tone of brief childhood memories. This is the past she is losing by regaining her health—the loss of attachments and roots that, while often gnarled and twisted, provided the spine which held her identity bent but upright. It is not only this loss that she mourns, but also the compounding loneliness that occurs after the "surgeon" has applied his scalpel, washes his hands and leaves the patient to fumble toward healing.

As a writer, Slater never washes her hands of her reader. While she perturbs comfortably held assumptions, raises the unanswerable, seamlessly slides in facts and educational information, Slater, mimicking the chemical action of Prozac, creates a "satin space" within which we can bear and consider the new and difficult. Change, whether it is the result of the ingestion of a pill or new awareness, is necessarily slow because it can be so full of grieving.

—*Karen Rosica*

Phantoms in the Brain: Probing the Mysteries of the Human Mind

by V.S. Ramachandran, M.D., Ph.D, and Sandra Blakeslee

William Morrow, 1998, 328 pp

As a boy, V.S. Ramachandran, M.D., Ph.D, professor and director of the Center for Brain and Cognition at the University of San Diego, was enthralled with the books of Charles Darwin and other 19th century scientists including Michael Faraday, author of the classic "Chemical History of a Candle." "There was no distinction at this time between academic and popular writing, but rather the notion that one could be deep and serious but completely accessible, all at once," explains the neuroscientist and best-selling author, Oliver Sacks, M.D., in the forward to "Phantoms in the Brain." It was Dr. Ramachandran's lifelong appreciation for popular science books that fueled the inspiration for this book. Along with co-writer Sandra Blakeslee, a science reporter for the New York Times, Ramachandran recounts his work with patients whose enigmatic neurological disorders cast light on the workings of the brain.

Although "Phantoms in the Brain" is co-authored, a strong, singular voice belonging to Ramachandran emerges. Ramachandran is an engaging narrator, whose down-to-earth persona is characterized by compassion for his patients and a sense of humor that enlivens the often-lengthy descriptions of neurological physiology and scientific experimentation.

Before taking the reader's hand and embarking on a fascinating odyssey into the deep recesses of the brain, Ramachandran is careful to point out that neurology is a field still in its infancy. Unlike the field of physics, which has Einstein's law of relativity and Newton's law of gravity, neuroscientists are still grappling with discovering a unified theory on the brain. While others have confirmed many of Ramachandran's findings, such as his research on phantom limbs, some of his work (on temporal lobe epilepsy, for example) is regarded as speculative.

In a chapter on phantom limbs—arms or legs that have sensation, even intense pain, after they've been amputated—Ramachandran offers compelling insight. In his opinion, phantoms occur by a reorganization of body image in the sensory cortex. In other words, an "imprint" of a limb's feeling can linger in the brain even after the limb is gone. Using a "virtual reality" device (a box with a transposing mirror), Ramachandran has had success helping some patients. When a patient sees their real limb transposed over the phantom, the brain can be "tricked" into "killing off" the phantom image.

Written in clear, unadorned prose, Ramachandran's book is built upon single-case narratives that go beyond describing unusual clinical conditions. One of his patients, Paul, suffers from temporal lobe epilepsy and claims God talks to him. Ramachandran does not dismiss Paul as crazy; instead, he uses this case to explore the fact that hidden in the limbic system (the area of the brain linked to our emotional responses), we may be programmed for religious experience.

After sustaining a head injury in a car crash, another patient, named Arthur, thinks his parents are imposters. In this case, Ramachandran takes the reader through the detective work that led him to diagnose Arthur as suffering from Capgras' syndrome. Ramachandran theorizes that a disconnection occurred between the temporal lobes (responsible for recognizing images such as a faces) and the amygdala (a pathway to the emotion-oriented limbic system). This kind of brain damage, Ramachandran surmises, could be the reason Arthur recognizes his parents' faces, but is unable to experience a familiar emotional response when he sees them. Arthur's only escape from this conflict would be to assume his parents were imposters.

Some of Ramachandran's most exciting ideas appear in the final chapter, where he attempts to answer far-reaching philosophical questions on the nature of the self and consciousness, speculating that these concepts may actually be recorded on specific regions of the brain.

In "Phantoms in the Brain," Ramachandran has created a rich feast for the intellect, a feast that is equally inviting, whether the reader is a familiar guest at the table or a neophyte who has sat down for the very first time.

—*Stephanie Susnjara*

Hare Brain, Tortoise Mind: How Intelligence Increases When You Think Less
by Guy Claxton   *Ecco Press, 1997, 247 pp*

British psychologist Guy Claxton's "Hare Brain, Tortoise Mind" is a fascinating exploration of the evolution of the human thought process and how we often ignore the more subtle machinations of our brains in our search for quick and clever solutions. Claxton, who received his doctorate from the University of Oxford for study on the structure of the human mind, and who has also studied with various Buddhist masters, refers to a wide range of scientific and psychological studies and relays informative, interesting and often humorous anecdotes to support and clarify his position. Although Claxton doesn't skimp on the scientific data, at heart he is a true storyteller, and it is his anecdotal style which makes "Hare Brain" such an entertaining and informative read.

Claxton explains that humans basically have two modes of thought—conscious or deliberate thought, and unconscious thought or the "undermind"—and that the Western world regularly dismisses the value of the unconscious for the instant answers that conscious thought can generate. "We have been inadvertently trapped in a single mode of mind that is characterised by information-gathering, intellect and impatience, one that requires you to be explicit, articulate, purposeful and to show your reasoning. ... But when this purposeful, justificatory, 'always-show-your-reasoning' attitude becomes part of the dominant default mode of the mind, it then tends to suppress other ways of knowing and makes

one skeptical of any activity whose 'point' you cannot immediately, consciously see."

Claxton asserts that when our brains have the time and space to consider problems and issues in a relaxed manner and the time to observe the world around us, our undermind goes to work. The undermind draws from our life experience and uses information stored in our brains which we don't always have instant access to. The use of our unconscious enables us to come up with more creative and often better solutions and ideas. Although he is quick to say that both modes of thought are necessary, it is the unconscious mind that is too often neglected in favor of conscious and deliberate decision-making.

"Only active thinking is regarded as productive. Sitting gazing absently at your office wall or out of the classroom window is not of value. Yet many of those whom our society admires as icons of creativity and wisdom have spent much of their time doing nothing. Einstein, it is said, would frequently be found in his office at Princeton staring into space. The Dalai Lama spends hours each day in meditation. Even that paragon of penetrating insight, Sherlock Holmes, is described by his creator as entering a meditative state 'with a dreamy vacant expression in his eyes.'"

Claxton explains his theories surrounding the undermind in great detail, using numerous metaphors to help the reader wade through the sometimes complicated scientific evidence of the brain's operations. He backs up his claims with varied examples from both scientific studies/experiments and numerous anecdotes and musings on the thought process from a great assortment of writers, philosophers, scientists and mathematicians. In his chapter, "Paying Attention," which discusses the importance of patient observation, Claxton spins through advice from a Zen master, an anecdote of a factory boiler repairman, musings by painter J. M. Whistler, an excerpt from a Sherlock Holmes novel to quotes from an essay by Freud. By telling story after story with a great deal of clarity and dry wit, Claxton adds layer upon layer of evidence proving the power of the unconscious in a completely engaging and colloquial fashion, all the while giving the readers time for their unconscious minds to digest the scientific material.

Claxton offers no quick fix for getting our unconscious minds in gear—"Hare Brain, Tortoise Mind" is not a touchy-feely, self-help book. He insists there needs to be a major shift in the way society works and learns before we can once again value the need for "empty" contemplation, for just letting our minds go sometimes. His entertaining storytelling, combined with his strong scientific argument, convinces the reader that it can be possible to live in a productive world while also taking the time to reflect and ponder, or to stare out the window and "think" nothing at all.

—*Kate Flaherty*

Kate Flaherty *is a Ph.D. student in English at the University of Nebraska-Lincoln and co-editor, with Hilda Raz, of "The Prairie Schooner Essay Anthology," forthcoming from the University of Nebraska Press.*

Karen Rosica *is a psychoanalyst in private practice in Denver and received her M.F.A. in creative nonfiction from Goucher College in August.*

Stephanie Susnjara *lives, writes and edits in New York City. She is pursuing an M.F.A. in creative nonfiction at Goucher.*

Sport Literate

Sport Literate, **Honest Reflections on Life's Leisurely Diversions** is documenting life outside the daily grind of making a living through nonfiction essays, poetry and interviews. The word *sport* has 14 definitions (we list them on our inside cover) and we explore each of them with allegoric writing that might surprise you. (We're not a jock chronicle.)

We invite you to discover us, read us, write for us and subscribe to our particular meditations on life's leisurely diversions. If you're short of change or still skeptical, ride the digital wave to: *www.avalon.net/~librarian/sportliterate/* for back issues, kudos and 3-D images of our cool hats. Pushovers and gamblers send $14 for a subscription (4 issues), $5.75 for a sample copy, or a SASE for writers' guidelines to: **Sport Literate, PO Box 577166, Chicago IL 60657-7166.**

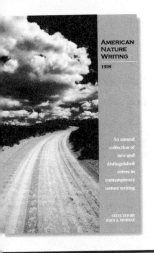

American Nature Writing 1999

SELECTED BY JOHN A. MURRAY

Now in its sixth year, this acclaimed series has become a leading showcase for contemporary nature writing, highlighting both new and distinguished voices. The eighteen selections show the rich variety of human responses to natural places and range geographically from the Tibetan Plateau to Baja California, from the woods of New England to the wilds of northern Alaska.

Paperback, $15.95

North Bank

Claiming a Place on the Rogue

ROBIN CAREY

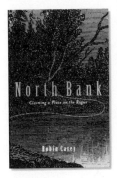

"Reading *North Bank* is almost as much fun as fishing. Carey reports the things so many outdoor writers miss—the things that, when noticed, give fishing joy and meaning and that, when ignored, render it just a 'sport,' like bowling... Here is the feel of a fresh steelhead punching your fly at the end of a run, the music of birds and waterfalls, the fragrance of spring meadows, the colors of canyons when sunlight spills over their rims—the how it was."
—Ted Williams, Editor-at-Large, *Audubon Magazine*
Hardcover, $19.95

Peace at Heart

An Oregon Country Life

BARBARA DRAKE

"This meditation on farm and countryside is a sweetly accurate, unpretentiously subtle portrait of a real place and people really living there. It offers the reader something rare and to be cherished: an honest description of happiness." —Ursula K. Le Guin
Paperback, $15.95

Available in bookstores or by calling 1-800-426-3797

Oregon State University Press

101 Waldo Hall, Corvallis, Oregon 97331
541-737-3166 • OSU.Press@orst.edu • http://osu.orst.edu/dept/press
Complete catalog and Authors' Guidelines available upon request

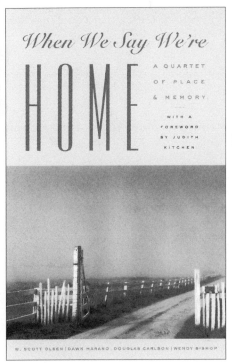
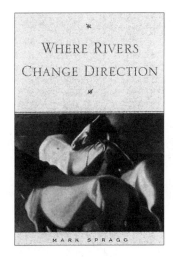

The Pregnancy Project
Encounters with Reproductive Therapy
Karen Propp

"Propp, who put off deciding to have a child until she was 39, recounts [her] struggles to have a child through reproductive technology.... Propp convincingly conveys the dashed hopes, despair and pure physical pain she experienced during the frequent injections and egg extractions. ... Propp finally became impregnated through an egg retrieval and embryo transfer and later gave birth to her son, Zohar. Couples with infertility problems will take heart from the author's laborious success story." — *Publishers Weekly*

$24.95 Hardcover edition   ISBN 0-8207-0302-8

What the River Means
Elizabeth Hodges

Through memorable story essays, Hodges reveals the importance of place in who we become and the importance of naming one's world in order to live well in it. The river is an omnipresent part of Hodges's written geography — whether she is fishing with her grandfather; or remembering the drowning of her 3-year-old neighbor, Billy; or relishing the joy of summer swims in the river, the feel of "cool water on sun-blushed skin."

"These are the essays of a genuinely gifted writer with a finely tuned ability to make the textures and sounds and tastes of youth come wildly alive in the adult mind." — Diana Hume George

$24.95 Hardcover edition   ISBN 0-8207-0294-3

The Last Settlers
Jennifer Brice
photographs by Charles Mason

"... Alaska native Brice explores how the original appeal of wilderness for two families was more a concept than a geography. ... [O]ffers a compelling and sobering analysis of the Last Frontier psyche." — *Publishers Weekly*

"Far from the glossy tourist brochures and finely directed videos, Brice and Mason cut *National Geographic* gloss to the bone. ... This is a fine collection for anyone seeking an armchair guide to wilderness settlement or to those for whom home is somewhere beyond." — *ForeWord Magazine*

$24.95 Hardcover edition   ISBN 0-8207-0290-0

DUQUESNE
UNIVERSITY PRESS
c/o CUPS, 750 Cascadilla St., Box 6525,
Ithaca, NY 14851. Toll free (800) 666-2211

romancing
the brain

tracking our obsession with the most complex object in the world

Sept. 18 - Nov. 21

OPENING PARTY

Sept. 17, 5:30 - 8 p.m.

PUBLIC PROGRAMS

Artists and the Brain
Sunday, September 19,
Discussion with the artists and *Creative Nonfiction* writers.
Moderated by guest curator Suzanne Ramljak.
FREE at pittsburgh center for the arts

The Diseased Brain
Sunday, October 10,
Discussion with artists, writers and medical researchers.
Moderated by history and philosophy of science professor
Peter Machamer.
FREE at carnegie science center

Emotions and the Brain
Saturday, October 30
Discussion with a visual artist, a theater artist and a
medical researcher. Moderated by psychiatry and
pediatrics professor Ron Dahl.
FREE at carnegie science center

PITTSBURGH|CENTER|FOR THE ARTS
fifth & shady avenues   t: 412/361-0873

experience the art of our times